be
THIN
Master your
EMOTIONS

Maurice Larocque M.D.

be
THIN
master your
EMOTIONS

Translated by Yves St-Pierre

Maurice Larocque Health Books
4335 Verdun Ave,
Verdun, Québec, Canada.
H4G 1L6
Tel.: (514) 769-7822

Published simultaneously in the United States of America.
FIRST EDITION

This book is dedicated to my patients who, through their confidence and support, encouraged me to write it and share with thousands of others the wonderful secrets of a happy and fulfilled life.

TABLE OF CONTENTS

The case histories presented in this book are true. Only the names have been changed in the interest of confidentiality.

Foreword

Be Thin, Master Your Emotions is the second in a trilogy of books on the psychological approach to the treatment of people who are suffering from or prone to obesity. In fact, everyone can benefit from the prescriptions for happiness this book has to offer.

For the sake of confidentiality, all names and ancillary details have been changed. In order to benefit fully from the present book, I would suggest you read the first in the series: **Be Thin through Motivation.** That way you will have a more rounded understanding of the wonderful modern psychological technique it makes available to you.

Once you've done the reading, you have to move into action. You must put into practice the techniques that have proven so valuable to so many others. And you would probably do well to re-read this book periodically, even if only a few pages at a time. Repetition is the key to success and to the happiness you deserve.

Maurice Larocque, M.D.

CHAPTER 1

THE POWER OF EMOTIONS

Compulsive eating

"I'm going crazy, I have no idea what I'm doing anymore. Yesterday I did something absolutely horrible. I consumed the entire content of my refrigerator, a whole cherry pie, a quart of ice cream, half a box of chocolate cookies and a quart of milk. I ate as if I'd never eat again. It was like a nightmare, but when it was all over the empty containers were there to prove it really happened. I feel like it's hopeless. When I start eating, I simply can't stop. Do you think there is any way I can get out of this, Doctor?"

Let's call her Fran. She's thirty-five and her story is like thousands of others. Mother of two, a seven year old boy and a five year old girl, she is the head nurse in the Intensive Care Unit of a major hospital. She had come to consult me about her weight problem. Over the last four years she had tried every method known to lose about twenty-two extra pounds.

In order to learn more about Fran, I introduced her to Bert, Bert is a computer that analyses the responses to a fifty question psychological evaluation. It takes about fifteen minutes to fill out. In effect Bert evaluates behaviour; it "weighs" what is going on inside the respondent's head and reveals the results in terms of mental or behaviour weight. The ideal score is the subject's ideal weight. The higher the score, the more the subject's behaviour needs to be modified. This tool allows the person to monitor his or her behaviour on a monthly basis. In addition, it gives the patient an ongoing personality profile that takes into account habitual behaviour, motivation, stress factors and emotional states.

Fran's initial results were very interesting. At 140, her mental weight was close to normal. Her profile revealed a well balanced and self-confident personality. Her motivation was excellent. Her living habits were quite good, except for her bouts of compulsive eating. Bert also revealed the source of the cravings and compulsive behaviour, emotional stress. Whereas the normal score for emotional stress is 30, her's was very high at 50. Two factors accounted for the high score: extreme perfectionism and a high level of guilt.

When I gave Fran her results, she relaxed and smiled: *"It's true, I'm very self-confident. That's why I do so well in everything I undertake except for losing weight. I can't understand it. It's so frustrating and it makes me very angry with myself."*

"In order to figure it out, we'll have to examine your behaviour, the thoughts and feelings that precede your compulsive reaction."

She interrupted:

"I'd rather concentrate on the future. I feel really unconfortable talking or even thinking about my compulsive eating. So if it's all the same to you, Doctor, I'd rather we not talk about it."

"I understand your reluctance, Fran. You feel guilty about your behaviour. You have dedicated your life to excellence, and

16

you can't accept your inability to control your compulsive eating.
But the only way to help you get rid of the compulsion is to exam-
ine your behaviour. To learn and progress from your past fail-
ures."

"That may be so, Doctor, but I haven't the slightest idea why
I did it. There's no excuse for the way I behaved yesterday. Every-
thing was going along fine, work, my children, my
marriage....everything. I really don't understand."

It's hard for Fran to go back over the incident. It's like an
open sore on her memory.

Reaction behaviour

Binge eating is usually related to emotional states. Re-
viewing Bert's analysis, we find that Fran is particularly vul-
nerable in that area.

"In the days before your last episode, were you subjected to
any undue frustrations or annoyances?"

"No, I can't think of anything."

"What about at home, was your husband or one of your chil-
dren sick or upset?"

"No, things couldn't have been better."

"How is your health?"

"Aside from my weight problem, I feel great, I jog and work
out twice a week and I also play racket ball once a week. I have to
stay in shape to get everything done the way I want to. And my
appearance is important to me. That's why I hate carrying around
these twenty extra pounds."

"How about work?"

"I was made head nurse in intensive care a month ago. I was
very surprised. I didn't think I'd get it because of my weight. I love
the work, but it's quite stressful. There's a lot of responsibility."

In fact, Fran's work was very demanding. She had twelve

17

nurses under her and she was responsible for the smooth operation of the I.C.U. Lately there's been a labour dispute involving the support staff. The union's pressure tactics had entailed a deterioration of patient services. Everybody, patients, nurses, doctors, felt the strain, especially Fran who was in charge of the unit. Faced with a situation beyond her control, she tried as hard as she could to maintain the best possible patient care. In the end, the patients weren't too inconvenienced. But Fran felt extremely frustrated after every shift.

"I find it appalling that a labour dispute can cause a deterioration in the care patients have a right to expect. It's absolutely intolerable. My parents taught me sound moral principles, among them a sense of responsibility and pride in work well done. I have to admit that I often find it frustrating to work with the kinds of attitudes you find today."

The day before her last bout of compulsive eating, Fran had had a confrontation with a union representative regarding essential services, Fran is a perfectionist who resists compromise. The more the union forced her to act against her principles, the higher her frustration level. In the end, without any idea why, she threw herself into her eating binge with complete abandon.

Automatic Responses

Here is one way psychologists break down the stages in a subject's behaviour:

Sequence   A-An **External Event** takes place
            B-that gives rise to an **Emotional Response**
            C-that, in turn, results in a form of **Behaviour.**

In Fran's case, what happened can be summarized as follows:

A-The **External Event**: she is forced by the union to compromise her principles.

B-The **Emotional Response**: She feels extremely frus-

18

trated.

C-The **Behaviour**: She has a bout of compulsive eating.

The first thing Fran must now understand is that her compulsive eating is an absolutely automatic response to the frustration. That is to say that neither her will nor her conscious mind are involved. It's a conditioned reflex she probably acquired in her earliest childhood.

"It's true, I remember, when I was little, as soon as I became irritated or frustrated my mother would give me a treat. I'm sure you're right. I often find myself going to the fridge without even thinking about it."

It should be noted that compulsive eating after a frustration is as automatic as pulling one's hand away from a flame once having been burned. It is the same kind of early childhood conditioning.

"I think I have a better understanding of why I eat compulsively in certain circumstances, but how can I break the habit, how can I overcome that kind of automatic response? It seems almost impossible."

"You're right, it's not easy to do. Emotions, especially when they are very intense, automatically trigger equally strong responses before the will can intervene. But when you are able to feel an emotional state coming on, or when it's less intense, you can then break the habit by changing your behavional response. For example, instead of eating, you might choose to go for a walk, to write down your frustrations or to start some other diversionary activity."

"Is there something that can be done when the emotion is intense and sudden? That's the way it usually is with me. You've helped me realize that with my responsibilities at home and on the job I'm frustrated more often than I thought."

The first thing I wanted was for Fran to overcome her guilt feelings about her compulsion. That's paramount. Fran mustn't feel guilty. She is the victim of a conditioned response, a habit, she can't be both a victim and guilty. And she can't begin to control her other emotions until she overcomes her guilt. Guilt is a negative feeling that can only result in negative self destructive behaviour.

Reflex Feelings

How can a person become less emotional? Only with difficulty, it seems.

I hear testimonies like Fran's every day. The majority of people seem to think themselves victims of their nervous systems. They give up and accept their sorry lot. Yet something can be done and it's not as difficult as many people believe. You simply have to understand how behaviour is determined and practice the techniques proposed in this book.

"But doctor, I've been trying to control myself for years; it's just stronger than I am. I tell myself this time don't get upset if the union rep is unreasonable, but as soon as I'm in the situation my resolve completely disappears. I get upset all over again."

"I understand what you're saying, Fran and you're right, emotions do arise automatically. Neither the will nor the conscious mind is involved. It's a reflex just like your compulsive eating."

Indeed, a very interesting experiment proved beyond a doubt that our emotional responses are acquired behaviour, habits, in fact.

Several years ago two researchers, Watson and Raynor, studied the behaviour of a nine month old child. The child liked mice and displayed absolutely no fear of the animals. He would stroke their fur and play with them. One day the researchers decided that every time the child was put into contact with the mice, they would subject him to the sharp and unpleasant sound of a gavel. Results were soon observable. Within a few days, each time the child was exposed to the mice and at the same time, the sound of the gavel, he would begin to cry and shy away from the animals which he no longer would even touch. He'd become afraid of mice.

Then researchers decided to eliminate the noise. The results were surprising; every time he was exposed to the mice he would become agitated, cry and shy away. He was still frightened. The child was then exposed to a piece of fur and the same results were observed. He was not only afraid of mice but also of anything that reminded him of them.

Watson and Raynor had effectively proven that emotional responses are acquired. But they didn't leave it at that. They felt that since they'd programmed the response, they could probably deprogram it. Within seven sessions, the child was no longer afraid. He was once again playing with the mice and stroking their fur.

Our emotional responses are therefore acquired habits that arise automatically in the presence of certain stimuli or sometimes even when we're simply reminded of these stimuli.

The important thing is: we can also lose these reflex emotional responses.

A Possible Approach

Since emotions arise automatically there is no sense in just asking someone to be less emotional.

Let's go back to our earliest model:

A.The **EXTERNAL EVENT**: Fran is forced by the union to operate under circumstances in which her principles are compromised. The situation is beyond her immediate control. She is free to express opinions but the final decision is not hers alone. She's forced to operate in a situation she can't change even though her demands may be fair.

B.The **EMOTIONAL RESPONSE**: A great deal of frustration arises **AUTOMATICALLY**. Unfortunately, she has little

21

control over these feelings.

C. The **BEHAVIOUR:** The response, also **AUTOMATIC,** is an eating binge. When the emotion is not too strong she may be able to divert her response to another activity. But when the feelings are intense, it's very difficult to alter the resultant behaviour.

So what can we do to eventually master our emotions?

Psychologist Albert Ellis offers a solution.

Here is his addition to the model:

A-The **EXTERNAL EVENT** gives rise to
B-Our **THOUGHTS** about the event, which in turn, gives rise to
C-The **EMOTIONAL RESPONSE** and the resultant **BE-HAVIOUR**

The additional fact is that our emotional response rests on our **THOUGHTS** process. That's why two individuals faced with the same situation react differently. For example, you and a friend are walking along the sidewalk; a man stops, laughs, then moves on. Your friend is deeply hurt while you laugh it off. The external event is the same, yet your emotional responses are diametrically opposed. Your friend is offended because she **THINKS** the stranger was laughing at her. You find the situation amusing because you **THINK** the individual was either unbalanced or on drugs, and certainly ridiculous.

The only way to alter our emotional responses is to work on the **THOUGHT** processes of which they are the result. Only then can we overcome the habit of reflex response.

The Automatic Thought Process

Let's look at Fran's behaviour.

"It's true, doctor," she admitted, *"every time I'm faced with*

an obstacle, I become upset particularly if my values are involved. Even when I try to reason with myself, it's beyond my control."

"You realize that we often can't avoid obstacles and irritations. They're a normal part of every day life."

"I know that, but it's not always easy to accept. Some injustices are very hard to deal with. Like the situation at the hospital, I can't accept that, for petty reasons, the union can disrupt the entire functioning of my department to the detriment of patient care." Her tone reflects the intensity of her feelings.

"I can see you getting upset all over again"

"I can't help it. Just talking about it makes my insides writhe. Don't you agree with me?"

"You're right to be concerned about the situation at the hospital. I absolutely agree with you there. But you're not right to make yourself sick over a problem that's beyond your control. All you're doing is creating a second insoluble problem."

"It's true. My binge eating has been on the increase and I hate myself for it."

"Even though you can't change the situation at the hospital," I added , *"you can control your reaction to it."*

What goes on in Fran's head when she's in a conflict situation with the union rep?

She automatically thinks that it's awful to use patients as hostages in a union/management conflict, that in fact, it is absolutely unacceptable, and that a person can't just stand by and watch that kind of blatant injustice.

Why does Fran think this way?

She comes from a good family where she learned strong moral standards and developed perhaps too strong a sense of perfectionism. As a child she was expected to excel in school, to be first in everything. At home it was the same thing. Everything was expected to run perfectly smoothly with everyone playing his or her part. Interpersonal relationships were run on principles of justice. At school, these same precepts were reinforced. As a catholic she was a member of religious groups that were equally uncompromising. She brought these values into her marriage. She strove to be a perfect spouse, Super Mom, an excellent housekeeper and a great nurse.

All this conditioning from an early age yielded a very competent person, but a rigid perfectionist. That's why, when a situation arises in which Fran feels she can't live up to the standards of perfection she has set for herself, even if it's not her fault and there is nothing she can do about it, she automatically becomes intensely frustrated.

"You're right, that's how I've always felt. So how can I change now", she asked.

An Islamic Example

When we're born, we have no thoughts. Our mind is like a blank slate. Our life experiences and the things we learn determine how we think. Just like programming a computer. Our parents are, of course, our primary programmers. That's why thought processes differ from individual to individual.

I recently saw a television report on an incident that occurred in an Arab country. The reporter was interviewing a man and a woman whose sister had been murdered a short time before. The brother and sister lived in a modern apartment with all the latest amenities.

The sister had been killed in unusual circumstances. She had had a lover whom she'd wanted to marry, but her father had arranged her marriage to one of her cousins. Some time after the wedding she ran off to join the man she loved. Tormented by remorse over her disobedience, she returned to the family home to beg her father's forgiveness. Three days later she was found dead.

The reporter asked the victim's brother if he knew who had killed her.

"I did," he answered. *"She was my own blood, but I had no choice. The family's honour was at stake. My father asked me to kill her and as the oldest son I had to. If I had to do it again, I'd do the same thing."*

The reporter then asked the sister what she thought of the situation.

"They were right, she had betrayed the family's honour and it was the only just thing to do."

To us Westerners it may seem unbelievable, even insane, for people, members of the same family, to behave in such a way. And yet they weren't born thinking this way. The way they think is a direct result of what their parents and their religion have been repeating to them all their lives.

The Ideal of Perfection

Fran was brought up in a totally different environment.

But she also thinks the way her parents taught her to. The things she has accepted as truths all her life have formed the basis of her own thought processes.

Fran has heard all her life that there's no room for compromise, that her performance and that of others must be beyond reproach, and that no form of injustice can be tolerated. Having been programmed this way from early childhood, she believes in this principle absolutely and it's very hard for her to consider changing.

A More Realistic Approach

"I've always liked things to be done well. What you're suggesting is not easy, doctor. Do you expect me to become less efficient in my work, less of a perfectionist with regard to my chil-

dren's needs and a less competent housewife?"

"Not at all. I believe there's always room for improvement. Ambition is a fine quality and I wouldn't want you to compromise your competence either as a nurse, a mother or a homemaker."

"Then what is it I'm supposed to change?"

"It's not your behaviour that needs changing, it's your all or nothing attitude. It would be great if everybody were beautiful, intelligent and healthy, and shared your sense of justice. Unfortunately, that's not the way it is. We have to strive for excellence while understanding that it can't always be achieved. That's what being realistic is all about."

It Would Be Great ...But

"You're right, of course. But even if I tell myself that nobody's perfect, that the union rep might not be so bad after all, my emotional reaction is still the same; I still become frustrated."

"You can't expect to change overnight a thought process that took 10, 20 or 30 years to acquire. To counteract the often repeated lessons you learned over the years, you have to tell yourself constantly that IT WOULD BE GREAT if everybody were perfect, if everybody shared my sense of justice BUT people have a right to be different, to make mistakes, even to commit injustices."

Only the constant repetition of the sentence: "It Would Be Great... But", particularly in conflictive situations, can lead to a more flexible thought process and a better control over emotional responses.

Obviously, if Fran finds herself in conflict with the union rep tomorrow she still won't be able to control her frustration. But if she keeps telling herself that it would be great if the union rep had a different attitude but that he has a right to feel as he does, within a few weeks she should be able to accept the situation. She won't like it any better, but it won't drive her to extreme frustration or to compulsive eating.

26

CHAPTER 2

CONTROLLING YOUR EMOTIONS

Mission Impossible?

"I'm extremely nervous, doctor, and there doesn't seem to be anything I can do about it."

"I was born emotional and I'm stuck with it."

"I've always been very edgy; I guess I just have to learn to live with it."

Every day I hear such statements of surrender to the difficulty of controlling one's nerves or emotions. Most people truly believe there's nothing to be done and that is very sad because it's absolutely untrue. In fact it was those very comments that prompted me to write this book. I hope to show these people how to live happier lives.

Nerves and emotions can be controlled. We saw in chapter one that emotional responses are acquired and automatic just like any habit. We aren't born either nervous or emotional. As we develop we acquire emotional responses to certain stimuli in our environment. The interesting thing is that like any habit, because we've acquired them we can also lose them.

"I don't understand."

A man comes to my office. He's slightly overweight, 34 years of age. He explains that he usually has no problem with food, but that once in a while an inexplicable craving comes over him. In fact he'd had an attack the day before his visit. He'd been to the theatre with his wife and had enjoyed an interesting and pleasant evening. When they got home, the food craving hit him. With further questioning, he admitted that although he enjoyed going to plays and shows very much, he felt strangely uneasy every time he stepped into a theatre or concert hall.

"I guess I worry for the performers and come to think of it, every time I go to a live performance I have one of my ridiculous food cravings."

So that was the first link, his cravings arose as the result of an emotion, a feeling of unease for the performers.

As I questioned him about his past, he told me that he used to play piano. One day he'd been pressed into service as accompanist for a young singer song-writer's début concert. The evening of the concert he was, of course, very nervous. Just as he launched into the intro to the first songe, his music sheet fell to the floor. What a disaster! The young audience laughed uproariously. The traumatized pianist gathered up his music sheet and started again. Needless to say the entire concert was a painful experience for the young musician.

As he told me his story I would see he was beginning to understand his strange behaviour. More than 15 years later, every time he set foot in a theatre, even if he didn't consciously make the association, he automatically relived his past experience and was prey to the emotion it evoked.

Such is human nature. The emotions we experience are stored in our subconscious. The way they're stored can best be understood by the following analogy, remember the juke-boxes that used to be found in restaurants and dance halls. The records were lined up and when you made your selection an arm would pick out your record and set it on the turntable. Our emotions are imprinted on our subconscious, and like so many records stand waiting to be selected. As soon as the slightest stimulus recalls the emotion, automatically the old record is played in all its intensity. Memory has nothing to do with the process. Regardless of whether or not you recall the original incident, the old record will automatically play without intervention from the conscious mind.

Another important thing to remember is that the intensity of the experience that triggers this sort of response can be minimal. It can be absolutely insignificant in comparison to the original experience. Just as long as it recalls, even unconsciously, the past event, the old emotional response will arise with almost its original impact. Maybe you've witnessed someone react to the loss of his or her dog. In such circumstances I've often observed emotional responses almost as intense as if the person had lost a close relative. When the process is triggered, the original record is played all over again.

But even if the person cannot immediately understand the cause of the emotional response, it doesn't mean an explanation and a solution don't exist.

Objection!

"Keeping yourself in too close check can be harmful. You can make yourself sick bottling everything up."

This kind of objection is often raised. It's based on a misunderstanding of the process involved in controlling the emotions.

What these people mean is that when a person is in the throes of an emotion it's better to express it, to get it out rather than try to suppress it and I agree with that. However, by controlling the emotions I mean stopping negative ones from arising. Everyone knows how awful it feels to be angry, afraid or extremely frustrated. In fact extreme emotional responses cause a stress reaction in our system. The adrenal glands automatically begin to produce adrenalin, noradrenalin and cortisol: stress hormones. In the presence of these hormones, our blood pressure rises and our heart rate increases. These reactions cause a burst of energy originally meant for the fight or flight required to ensure survival. But in the modern world the need for a physical reaction to stress has been greatly reduced, and this excess energy remains in the body where it can harm various organs. This may give rise to a number of symptoms: stomach ulcers, high blood pressure, tension, headache, fatigue, insomnia. In fact some research shows a possible link between stress and cancer.

Clearly, negative emotions and the resultant stress must be controlled.

"Life without emotions would be dull."

I hear that kind of remark sometimes as well. I'm not talking about becoming robots devoid of feelings and emotions. Only destructive emotions which tend to weaken and age a person must be controlled.

Positive emotions fill one's life with warmth, enthusiasm and joy. This we have to learn to cultivate.

"Not Me!"

During one of my weight loss courses, one of the students, 59 years old Jean asked what psychology had to do with the treatment of obesity. She didn't consider herself to be an emotional person or particularly tense. She just liked eating. In spite of my explanations, she just couldn't understand what the mind had to do with weight problems.

So I had her meet Bert, my behaviour monitor, (a computerized psychological test). The results were surprising: her emotional quotient reached 57, normal readings being below 30. The factors involved were a high degree of perfectionism, 80 points out of a maximum 100, and a marked tendency to dramatize events, 62 points out of a possible 100.

When I told Jean the results she looked perplexed. From my office she went directly to the psychology section of a nearby library. She brought home and read everything she could find on perfectionism and the tendency to dramatize. She was stunned. She fit the descriptions to a T. Even though she was highly educated and a teacher, at 59 she still didn't know herself!

Predictably, her reaction was dramatic: *"This is terrible; I've been highly neurotic for goodness knows how long and I didn't even realize it."* But because she was willing to change, in spite of her age, she was able to say to me some time later: *"You're the one person who has helped me most in my life."*

It's a constant source of amazement to me how poorly people know themselves. They acquire habits from childhood and take for granted that their behaviour is absolutely normal. Far from being in control of their lives, they are, in fact, victims of their reactions.

A highly energetic 50 year old woman comes to consult me about her diet. She manages a large department store, is active in many social groups and is a caring and efficient home maker.

After examining her and questioning her about her health, I gave her my verdict: *"You've been suffering from mi-*

graines for years and taking medication regularly; you have stomach ulcers for which you also regularly take medication. You're a highly stressed individual and something should be done about it as soon as possible."

"I'm not tense at all, Doctor. I love my family, my work and my social activities.I lead a busy life, it's true, but I'm not overly stressed."

It took a few weeks before she began to understand: "You're right. I'm extremely tense all the time. ever since you brought it up I've been more tuned into my body. When I'm driving my arms are always stiff. At work, whenever there's a problem I feel a burning sensation in my stomach or I get a blinding headache."

"Would you say you're a perfectionist?"

"No, not at all."

Yet everything she did had to be just perfect. She wanted everybody around her to be happy: her employees, her colleagues, her children and her husband. If any of these people were depressed in any way, she felt personally responsible and would try everything to cheer them up. In spite of her sunny disposition and her positive attitude, she was living under terrible stress every day and it was destroying her health. In expecting everyone around her to be happy, she was being too much of a perfectionist. And in spite of the signals her body was sending her, she didn't even realize it!

Do You Suffer From Stress?

On a separate piece of paper, write the number that corresponds to the frequency with which you experience each of the following symptoms.

Write: 0- for never.
          1- for occasionally (1 or 2 times a month.)
          2- for quite frequently (up to once a week).
          3- for frequently (more than once a week).

Don't write your responses in the book so you won't be influenced when you check your stress level again in a few weeks..

Question 1:
Other than when you're exercising, do you sometimes experience one or more of the following symptoms: Shortness of breath, palpitations or chest pain?
Answer:_____

Question 2:
Do you suffer from occasional neck or lower back pain that can't be attributed to an illness or other anomaly?
Answer:_____

Question 3:
Is your jaw tight?
Answer:_____

Question 4:
Is your throat dry?
Answer:_____

Question 5:
Is your forehead lined?
Answer:_____

Question 6:
Are your hands and feet cold and clammy?
Answer:_____

Question 7:
Do you get hot flushes not attributable to some obvious cause like physical exertion or menopause?
Answer:_____

Question 8:
Do you sometimes perspire without physical exertion?
Answer:_____

Question 9:
Do you suffer from abnormal fatigue?
Answer:_____

Question 10:
Do you sometimes have tremors?
Answer:_____

Question 11:
Do you have digestive problems?
Answer:_____

Question 12:
Do you feel dizzy?
Answer:_____

Question 13:
Do you feel numbness in your hands, your feet or both?
Answer:_____

Question 14:
Do you ever faint?
Answer:_____

Question 15:
Do you have trouble sleeping?
Answer:_____

Now add up your score.

If you scored between 0 and 5, there are three possibilities:

1- You answered the questionnaire incorrectly; please do it over more carefully.

2- Perhaps you are not tuned in to your body and you've been accepting as normal the signals of stress it's been sending out.

3- Or maybe you are a very passive person who lacks stimulation. Too much stress is harmful but a total lack of stress is death.

If you scored between 6 and 10, you are absolutely normal. Stress is not a problem for you right now. You are dealing with it very well. Congratulations.

If your score was between 11 and 15, you are normal but you have to be careful not to exceed your limits. Learn to relax, avoid overextending yourself and remain active. A positive life style will allow you to enjoy life to the fullest.

If you scored between 16 and 25, you are suffering from stress. You should immediately undertake remedial action. Chapter 3 will provide you with all the means necessary. The situation is serious. Don't waste any time.

If your score was 26 or more, you are extremely tense. Your life is considerably affected by stress. Serious physical symptoms are on the point of appearing if they have not already. Don't lose hope. Heed the advice offered in this book and consult a specialized health professional.

Are You An Emotional Person?

Stress and emotions are two distinct but often related entities. A stressful situation can often give rise to such emotions as fear, frustration or even guilt. As well, emotions can bring on stress symptoms such as palpitations or perspiration. The object of this second questionnaire is to help you better understand what is going on within yourself.

On a separate sheet write the number for each question that best represents what you think. Later you'll be able to take the test again without being influenced by your earlier response.

For the test to be valid, you must answer all the questions spontaneously and truthfully. Answer the questions on your own. Remember that there are no right or wrong answers. The only purpose of the test is to help you better understand yourself.

Question 1:

I never seem to have enough time to get everything done.

0: No, I have all the time I need
1: I sometimes run out of time
2: I often run out of time
3: I never have enough time.

Answer:_____

Question 2:

I expect a lot from others and I'm often disappointed even over small matters.

0: Absolutely untrue
1: sometimes true
2: quite often true
3: Absolutely true.

Answer:_____

Question 3:

I get involved in very few activities and never unless I'm sure of success.

0: Absolutely untrue
1: sometimes true
2: quite often true
3: absolutely true.

Answer:_____

Question 4:

I'm very demanding of myself.

0: No, never
1: sometimes
2: quite often
3: always

Answer:_____

Question 5:

When I make a mistake, I forget about it immediately.

0: Always
1: usually
2: Yes, but with difficulty

3: I have a great deal of difficulty forgetting about my mistakes.

Answer:_____

Question 6:

There is a time and place for everything and these should be respected.

0: Completely disagree.

1: somewhat disagree

2: somewhat agree

3: absolutely agree.

Answer:_____

Question 7:

I'm very sensitive and I'm often aggressive in order to fend off attack.

0: Completely disagree

1: somewhat disagree

2: somewhat agree

3: Absolutely agree.

Answer:_____

Question 8:

I become extremely upset when I learn someone doesn't like me.

0: No, not at all

1: I feel badly but I'm not particularly upset

2: I'm quite upset

3: I'm very upset.

Answer:_____

Question 9:

There is no justice. It's always the same people who succeed. I never get a chance.

0: Completely disagree

1: somewhat disagree

2: somewhat agree

3: absolutely agree

Answer:_____

Question 10:
When I'm faced with a problem, I try to look at the positive side.

0: always
1: usually
2: sometimes
3: rarely.

Answer:_____

Question 11:
I feel on the brink of some misfortune.

0: Never
1: sometimes
2: usually
3: always

Answer:_____

Question 12
When a person has not succeeded at something, things aren't likely to change when (s)he is 40 or 50.

0: completely disagree
1: somewhat disagree
2: somewhat agree
3: absolutely agree.

Answer:_____

Question 13:
I have a lot of energy but few interesting activities into which to channel it. (regardless of cause).

0: Never true
1: sometimes true
2: quite often true
3: very often true

Answer:_____

Question 14:
I take on other people's problems as if they were my own.

0: Never

1: sometimes
2: quite often
3: very often
Answer:_____

Question 15:
Being by myself doesn't bother me.
0: Never bothers me
1: sometimes bothers me
2: often bothers me
3: always bothers me.
Answer:_____

Now total your score.
If you scored between 0 and 5 there are two possibilities:

1- You answered the questionnaire incorrectly. Please do it again more carefully.
2- You are not in tune with your behaviour, You probably don't know yourself very well. You've been behaving automatically for many years and you can't see any alternative. Your life is probably rather dull. You would do well to spice it up.

If you scored between 6 and 10 you are emotionally very well balanced. Keep it up; you've found a winning combination.

If you scored between 11 and 15, you are normal and in control of your emotions. However, you should examine some of your behaviour and ideas. You could have a tendency to lose control of your emotions in certain difficult situations. By keeping a close check on yourself, particularly in such circumstances, you shoud be able to avoid major problems.

If you scored between 16 and 25, you are a rather emotional person. You should waste no time in doing everything you can to regain control of your emotions. This book will prove an excellent guide. The quality of your life should improve considerably.

If you scored 26 or more, you are an excessively emotional person. Your quality of life is greatly impaired. However, don't give up; you are not beyond hope. Put into practice all the advice offered in this book. Read it often and consult a specialized health professional.

Overall Evaluation

Look at your results on both questionnaires and note which one is the highest.

Then try to assess which is the cause of the other. Does stress bring on a strong emotional response or do your emotions cause your stress? It is essential to work on the cause of your problems if you want to achieve long lasting results.

As you read through the following chapters, particularly Chapter 4, try to identify your own patterns of behaviour and ways of thinking. Then apply the techniques suggested.

Once a month repeat the two diagnostic tests as objectively as possible. That way you'll be able to monitor and be encouraged by your progress. Don't look back at your previous responses before you fill in the questionnaires. Compare results only after you've filled them in. An improvement of only a few points indicates significant success. You can't expect to change dramatically from one day to the next.

CHAPTER 3

THE 5 PHASES OF THE TREATMENT

Phase one:
A Sound Mind In A Healthy Body

The first thing to consider in dealing with stress and emotional problems is the person's physical conditon. There is no sense trying to improve a person's nervous condition if he or she is in terrible physical shape.

Let's take an example: you probably own a battery operated electric calculator. What happens when the batteries run down? When you add 2 + 2 it rarely comes up 4. The device appears to be working, numbers light up but the results are wrong. The solution: new batteries.

The human body works in somewhat the same way: the body provides energy to the brain. When the body is unable to provide sufficient energy, the nervous system doesn't work as efficiently. A minor setback can become a major catastrophe. We can't add 2 + 2 and come up with 4. The ancient Greeks were right when they used to promote a sound mind in a healthy body.

Rest

The first and most essential condition for a healthy body is adequate rest. Without rest, it's impossible to control your emotions. Think of your behaviour when you are tired. Nothing seems to go right and the slightest annoyance becomes a huge problem. You feel like dropping everything, and forget about solving problems or understanding yourself when you're exhausted. The only thing you can do is get some rest. You have to recharge your batteries and only sleep can do it. You might have noticed how, after a good night's sleep, a problem that seemed insuperable was really trivial. When the batteries are recharged your mental computer works well again.

In general, human beings require 7 or 8 hours of sleep per night. Sleep allows the body to rebuild and regenerate strength. Some people who come into my office claim to be in good shape with only 3 or 4 hours of sleep per night. The difficulty is that a person can become accustomed to a lack of sleep and not experience any of the negative effects of sleep deprivation for a long time. However, they mustn't be fooled. Sooner or later it will catch up with them.

Ideal Weight

The second condition for achieving a sound mind in a healthy body is maintaining your ideal weight. This may surprise some people but the evidence is irrefutable.

Some time ago, Mark, a businessman, showed up at my office. He was in a pathetic state. Sixty-six pounds overweight due to a poor diet, he suffered from hypoglycemia. His episodes were marked by frantic hunger, trembling, perspiration and aggressiveness. They were a result of low blood sugar and could occur one or more times a day. He confided

42

that his business, he owns a medium sized trucking company, was not going very well, that he was burned out and that he wanted to sell the company. A few months later, after he had lost about forty pounds, he admitted that since he'd started dieting, he felt rejuvenated and very energetic. There was no longer any question of selling the company since sales figures had practically doubled. When I last heard, he was on the point of buying out one of his competitors.

It can be argued that some obese people do very well. It's undeniable. But think what these people could do with all the extra energy if they lost weight.

Here is what Sandra had to say after she had lost sixty-six pounds: *"Before, I was always angry. The moment I got up in the morning and saw myself in the mirror my mood would sour. I snapped at the kids all day long. I did almost nothing productive. I could barely do my housework. I was so tired I'd just think: to hell with it, I didn't care about anything. By the end I wasn't even making dinner for my husband and children. Today I'm a different person, very little ever upsets me. I am more patient with the kids and the atmosphere around the house is much more peaceful. The kids also seem less agitated. I know I was the problem. Now I am particularly excited; I start a part time job next week. A few months ago, If anyone had said I'd be working, I would never have believed it."*

Physical Activity

The third condition for achieving a sound mind in a healthy body is physical activity. We saw in the previous chapter how the stress we undergo creates a burst of energy that requires an outlet in the form of physical activity. If such energy is not allowed to dissipate through muscular activity it remains within the body where it can attack various vital organs.

Yesterday a twenty-five year old woman came to my office. She'd just taken "Bert" (a computerized test to evaluate personal behaviour). The results showed a great deal of stress and virtually no physical activity. When I suggested as part of her weight loss and stress control program that she immediately undertake some form of physical activity, she said: *"when I get home from work at night, I'm exhausted, I couldn't think of physical activity. Even weekends I don't feel up to it because I'm still too tired. Most of my spare time is spent sleeping."*

Indeed, primarily because of the stress she suffers, this young woman does feel extremely exhausted after a day's work. She is so tense that each day she builds up the same amount of energy as most people do in two days. No wonder she is exhausted. As a secretary, she doesn't do physical work so all this excess energy is detrimental to her. The first thing she has to do is exercise. It will be the best form of relaxation for her. Excessive sleep, more than nine hours, is almost as bad as not enough.

Try it yourself. After a day's work muster up all your courage and do some fairly demanding physical activity, exercise. Enough to work up a good sweat. You can skip rope, dance, jog, cycle, whatever you like. You may be surprised to find that after fifteen minutes you'll feel more rested.

A lot of research has been done on the relationship between physical activity and psychological well being. The results are conclusive: people who exercise regularly, at least 20 minutes, three times a week, are calmer, less emotional, more creative and generally more successful. And we now understand why. Physical activity fosters in the brain the secretion of hormones known as endorphins.

Endorphins are natural hormones that have some of the properties of morphine, the pain killing drug. Both stimulating and relaxing, endorphins promote a feeling of well being and reduce pain.

The choice of physical activity is very important. Choose

one that is enjoyable to you and appropriate to your age and physical conditon. Walking is a simple and very relaxing exercise. It should be done 4 or 5 times a week at a good clip for 30 to 60 minutes.

Physical activity is the best medicine I know for frazzled nerves. No one can afford not to do some form of exercise.

Phase Two:
Relaxation

In today's frantic world, everyone appreciates the need to relax. Unfortunately, few people do. Excuses are varied: "I don't have the time", "It doesn't work for me", "I don't know how."

Anybody can relax. The lack of time excuse is complete nonsense; once you're relaxed you can get your work done twice as quickly and efficiently.

And it can work for anyone. Certainly some people relax more readily than others. If it takes you a little longer to feel the benefits of relaxation, it's probably because you were very tense to begin with. Keep up your relaxation exercises and you'll soon feel the results. And be sure to pick a relaxation technique that's well suited to you. There are a number to choose from. If one isn't working try another. You'll soon find the one that's most appropriate.

The excuse of not knowing how won't stand up after you've read the following. Doctors J.H. Schultz of Germany and Luthe of Montreal have demonstrated the processes involved in relaxation. When the muscles are relaxed, a message is sent to the brain which in turn relaxes and brain waves slow down. As the cycle continues the relaxed brain further relaxes the muscles and so on.

Relaxation Activities

Numerous activities foster relaxation. Listening to soft music is certainly among the most popular. The magic of music has been recognized for ages.

Set aside periods of at least twenty minutes 4 or 5 times a week to listen to some soft music you particularly enjoy.

Reading can also help you unwind. Choose reading material that is restful. Reading and listening to music may be done together to heighten the effect.

Walking at an easy pace in a suitable environment can be very beneficial. You should walk for at least half an hour, 4 or 5 times a week.

Relaxation Techniques

Many worthwhile methods are available, two of the better known ones are Yoga and Transcendental Meditation. If you feel like trying these techniques or if you're already practicing them, go right ahead. They have proven their effectiveness.

Be Thin By Suggestion

That's the name of a program I've recorded on 4 cassettes that include numerous relaxation techniques and suggestions for all types of individuals. I put the program together three years ago and since then it has achieved astonishing results.

Everyone can choose the most appropriate type of relaxation, and for those days when 20 minutes is too long, 5 minute abbreviated versions are included. Specially chosen relaxing music is present throughout. The greatest asset of the program is that it can be adapted to each individual's specific needs.

Here is a list of the topics treated in **"Be Thin By Suggestion."**

1 – Autogenic relaxation, length 20 minutes.
2 – Autogenic relaxation with weight loss suggestions, length 20 minutes.
3 – Progressive relaxation, length 20 minutes.
4 – Progressive relaxation with weight loss suggestions, length 20 minutes.
5 – To master Short relaxation technique, length 5 minutes.

List of suggestions:
6 – To be thin, length 6 minutes.
7 – To take one day at a time, length 6 minutes.
8 – To eliminate guilt, length 6 minutes.
9 – To eliminate food deprivation, length 6 minutes.
10– To eliminate the taste for sweets, length 6 minutes
11– To eliminate the taste for fatty foods, length 6 minutes.
12– To be more assertive, length 6 minutes.
13– To master your emotions, length 6 minutes.
14– To demystify the importance of food, length 6 minutes.
15– To reward yourself positively, length 6 minutes.
16– To be more assertive, length 6 minutes.
17– To be more active, length 6 minutes.
18– To stay thin, length 6 minutes.
19– To stop nibbling, length 6 minutes.
20– To stop smoking, length 6 minutes.
21– To eliminate the desire for alcohol, length 6 minutes.
22– To increase self-esteem, length 6 minutes.
23– To increase self-confidence, length 6 minutes.
24– To believe in your success, length 6 minutes.

If you want more information on techniques to help you unwind without using the cassettes, I refer you to my book "BE THIN THROUGH MOTIVATION", particularly the chapter on Alpha power, p. 225 onward.

If your stress score was high, waste no time in beginning a suitable program. Within a month, when you do the test again, you'll see a marked improvement.

Who Can Do Without?

A young mother, to whom I'd suggested a relaxation program, talks about her experience:

"I have two children but I still have to work. When I come home at the end of the day I'm absolutely exhausted. I want everybody to just leave me alone. Before I took up the relaxation program, I used to fight with the kids all the time. Now when I get home, I shut myself in my room with my cassettes and unwind for twenty minutes. When I come out of my room I'm a new person. I feel full of energy. I get along much better with the kids and they're a lot less hyper too. I was the one who was making them tense."

This young woman obviously needs her relaxation. But who doesn't?

It takes a bit of commitment of course, but the results are so important to the quality of our lives. It's been estimated that five minutes of deep relaxation is worth a full hour of sleep. I readily admit that I can't do without it.

Phase Three: Letting Off Steam

We know from experience that our emotions are most often automatically and instantly aroused as a result of some annoyance. Before we can do anything to control it we may find ourselves suffering from a stress reaction. Our heart rate has increased and our blood pressure is up.

We must therefore, learn to let off steam in a healthy way.

The best way to do this is through muscle contractions,

exercise. We saw earlier how exercise is the best way to dissipate the energy created by stress. That's why women under stress will sometimes start shifting furniture around. Physical exercise is the most natural and efficient way of letting off steam. The greater the stress the more intense the exercises should be. People who are ill or in poor physical condition should, of course, take care to remain within the bounds of their ability.

Certain activities are rarely harmful - brisk walking, jogging, lifting moderate weights or even beating on a pillow or mattress.

The second way of leting off steam is writing. Jot down everything that comes into your mind, even your most hostile feelings about the person or situation that brought on the stress. Don't be concerned about the logic or the accuracy of what you're writing. Just let off steam. And don't censure yourself. If you feel like using foul or harsh language, go ahead. Once you've played out your frustration, you can always tear up what you've written. And you should not feel any guilt about it. It's normal for human beings to have aggressive feelings sometimes. And it doesn't hurt anyone, but don't forget to destroy what you have written.

The third way to let off steam is through internal monologue. Last year my son, who was then 11, came home from his first day back at school in tears. He was totally dejected and said he never wanted to go back. I finally gathered that his new teacher had been rather zealous in establishing his authority. The students would have to be well behaved at all times and succeed in everything or face serious consequences. My son's reaction was understandable. He didn't see how he could live up to his new teacher's expectations. As I chatted with him I suggested that he simply continue doing his best as he'd always done. What was important was not to satisfy the teacher but to work well for his own satisfaction. He was studying for himself not to please his teacher. At the same time, I assured him that we were proud of him and of the work he'd done in the past.

The next day when he came home from school he was beaming. "Was your teacher in better spirits to-day?" I asked. "Not really, but when he started to yell and threaten us I stopped listening and just repeated to myself: Go ahead and have a bad mood again. Instead of feeling like crying, I felt like laughing out loud. I told my friends about it and they did the same thing. We all had a good laugh."

I met a couple in their fifties one time when I was travelling. The wife was contantly criticizing the husband about everything. When I inquired, the husband told me they'd been married 27 years and that they'd never had any marital problems.

When I expressed my surprise in light of his wife's behaviour, he admitted she'd always been like that but said he'd developed a way of dealing with it whereby he silently answered her back, often sharply. He knew his wife well, he appreciated her for her many qualities and he'd come up with this way of dealing with his frustration over her constant criticism. For the rest of the trip, every time his wife nagged him, he'd point to his forehead, meaning that he was answering her back and getting rid of his frustration. Interior monologue is a very interesting technique and a skill well worth developing to help you cope with any number of potentially irritating situations.

Again, whatever you say to yourself can't possibly hurt the other person. And the situation is resolved much more quickly and easily than if you had responded out loud.

Incidentally, when my son's teacher got over his first day of jitters, he had changed his attitude and turned out to be a fine teacher indeed.

Phase Four:
The STOP Technique

As you examine your behaviour, you'll notice that your brain can only think of one thing at a time. Your thoughts can skip from one thing to another quite quickly but at any given time your brain can only handle one thought.

You will also notice that when you're thinking of something pleasant you feel good and your body is relaxed. When you're thinking of something unpleasant, you feel badly and you become tense.

It would seem, then, that you can control your emotions and your state of being by properly selecting your thoughts. And you can master your thoughts. Try this: stop reading and think about your next holiday or about some activity you especially enjoy. You've just proven that you can control your thoughts.

Some people don't agree.

"It's easy enough to control my thoughts when everything is fine but when I am preoccupied by a problem negative thoughts can take over. Sometimes they are impossible to get rid of. They are like an obsession."

Admittedly it is more difficult to control your thoughts when you're worried about something but it can be done. It's just a question of practice.

I particularly recommend the **STOP** technique. When you feel yourself becoming overwhelmed by stress and negative feelings, just say **STOP**, out loud if possible. In fact as loudly as you can. At the same time try to visualise a **STOP** sign. Then quickly turn your thoughts to a setting or a situation that fosters peace and serenity. It must be one that means a lot to you and that you associate with positive feelings.

At the beginning the effects might be short lived and you might have to repeat the exercise several times a day. But after a few days of practice you'll find that the periods of relaxation will be longer.

The success of this technique, then, depends on the choice of an image heavily charged with positive feelings and on its frequent use. If you practice the technique often and consistently, after about three weeks your brain should begin to spontaneously stop negative thoughts and automatically redirect your thinking to a positive image.

One of my friends, a high powered executive, explains how he deals with stress during important business transactions.

"When I feel under a great deal of stress and start having doubts and fears, I use the STOP technique and I tell myself that money is less important than my health. I imagine myself jogging barefoot along the seashore on a beautiful sunny day.

The effect is instantaneous. I feel relaxed and I can carrry on with my business."

Try it yourself. Concentrate and imagine in DETAIL the positive image and the feelings it arouses. Choose the image ahead of time so you can call it up quickly when the need arises. Remember that only practice can lead to quick and consistent results.

Phase five:
Prevention Rather Than Cure

The ultimate goal in controlling your emotions is to stop negative feelings from arising. It's easy to say: don't be so emotional; you should control your feelings or there's no reason to be so frustrated. Unfortunately, it's easier said than done.

This chapter is crucial in that it sets out the means of

controlling your emotions. Just about anyone can become less emotional by using the techniques that follow. These methods have proven themselves effective but they can't work without constant practice.

The first thing you have to accept if you hope to be less emotional one day is that, in spite of your good intentions and your new insights, you're bound to continue to experience negative feelings for some time. To know is not enough. A period of consistent and frequent practice on your part is required.

Learning From Your Mistakes

Surprisingly, the only way to progress in the control of emotions is through negative experiences. If over the next month, you find yourself in no unpleasant or stressful situations, you will no doubt feel good, but it won't mean that you've become any better at controlling your emotions. Don't be surprised or disappointed if the next time you're faced with a difficult situation, you don't react as you might have wished. Consider it a chance to learn from your mistakes.

It's the only way to progress.

Learning To Know Yourself

In learning to control your emotions, you'll necessarily make mistakes and experience negative emotions. The key is to use these situations to understand yourself better and to move ahead.

In chapter 1 we were introduced to the model proposed by Doctor Albert Ellis:

A- An external event

B- automatically gives rise to our thoughts about the event

C- which result in our feelings and behaviour.

Thus every negative emotional experience becomes a good opportunity to adapt this model to your personal case. Your ultimate goal is to identify the **THOUGHT** patterns to which the situation gives rise.

If you are unable to define clearly the **THOUGHT** you have about the situation you'll never be able to soften or change it and thereby prevent the negative emotional reaction.

You can't change what you don't know. The first step then, is to identify the cause: the negative or too rigid thinking.

Paper and Pencil

In order to clearly and objectively define your thinking you must jot down the A-B-C sequence of the model given above.

I have been treating Claire, a 55 year old teacher, for a weight loss problem. She had been doing well for several weeks when things suddenly changed.

"I don't know what happened, doctor, but this week I couldn't stop nibbling."

I suggested she keep a personal dietary diary.

The following week she reported:

"As I recorded what I was eating I became aware that over the past two weeks I've been feeling frustrated, so I did what you'd suggested. For the C- I wrote that for two weeks I've been feeling frustrated and I've been nibbling. Then I asked myself why and I realized that I knew. My husband had lost his job exactly two weeks ago. So I filled in the A - my husband's layoff. Then asked myself what I thought about the situation. Of course I was disappointed for my husband, who'll soon be sixty, especially since he wasn't taking it very well. On the other hand, we have enough money and my husband can use the rest. In fact, now we might be

54

able to do some of the things we've always wanted to do. When I'd filled in the B- I feel disappointed for my husband but I'm also looking forward to our new life, I felt relieved. Ever since then I've been back on my diet and I've stopped nibbling."

Have you ever noticed how easy it is to understand someone else's behaviour and to give him or her advice? That's because you can be more objective about a situation in which you're not directly involved.

When you objectify your problem by writing it out and breaking it down into A-B-C, you can deal with it as you would if it were someone else's problem. It will take on more realistic proportions and you'll be able to deal with it objectively.

You'll never learn to control your emotions unless you are prepared to use your paper and pencil every time you have an unpleasant emotional experience.

The Power Of Repetition

Once you have identified the unrealistic thinking behind your emotional response, your problems are not yet over. Knowing the negative is essential but you also have to imprint the positive thought pattern or image you wish to substitute. You must put the theory into practice.

You should program yourself several times a day, every time you have a negative emotional experience, by repeating to yourself the positive thought for at least 21 days. Repetition is the key to success.

A few years ago a soft drink company carried out the following experiment. Since the costs of television advertising were huge, and since the product was selling very well, it was decided to cut out the several daily television commercials for a period of three monhts. The object was simply to keep more of the profits. The experiment was tried in a limited viewing area. At the beginning of the experiment the soft drink in question was the leading seller in the area. At the end of three months it had dropped to seventh place. Needless to say the T.V. commercials were reinstated. The interesting thing is that even though the consumers were still aware of the brand, they'd stopped buying it. Only repeated messages influence behaviour.

The same principle applies when it comes to changing your thought patterns or behaviour. The big corporations have known this for a long time and what works for them will work for you. You just need a different message. Whatever message is repeated often enough, good or bad, will become your new way of thinking and will soon seem absolutely normal.

When you first start repeating to yourself the new thought patterns you want to imprint. They'll seem strange and awkward to you. But within three weeks they'll seem absolutely natural. You'll have acquired a new thinking habit.

Mental Jogging

Some might say it's exhausting to be constantly repeating positive messages to yourself. What they don't understand is that it's no harder than repeating negative messages to yourself. Once you've acquired the habit, the effort is the same. The problem is that too many people have acquired negative thought habits. Bear in mind that an individual talks to himself at an estimated rate of 1200 words a minute. So why not develop the habit of talking to yourself positively as a sort of mental jogging. Your brain needs exercise in much the same way that your body does. Neglect your exercises and you're soon out of shape.

Recidivism

Francine is a 32 year old legal secretary. As a participant in my behaviour and motivation program she lost a lot of weight and she learned to control the emotions that were triggering her eating compulsion. Here is a testimony her husband recently wrote to her: "You have more self-confidence, you are more measured in your speech, you listen rather than jump to conclusions, you're more understanding and less jealous and you're more enthusiatic about trying new activities."

The new thought pattern she was working on was this: "If you can't change a person or a situation, then accept it as it is" She had truly acquired the habit of saying this to herself everytime she found herself in a conflict situation. *"I really wonder if it was all worth it."* she said. *"I put on weight this week and I hate myself. All my bad habits are back."*

Indeed Francine did seem to have gone back to her old habits. And it was to be expected. Any physical or emotional habit a person has only recently overcome can appear when it's least expected. They usually show up again when the person is run down or ill or under severe stress. Francine's boss had criticized her work for the first time in 5 years. She'd been unable to deal with the criticism and had run to the refrigerator the way she used to.

Recidivism is a normal part of the process. The first thing to do is to accept it as normal. If you don't allow yourself to be discouraged by the relapse, the old habit disappears again very quickly, often within a few hours or a few days, because it has lost its base.

Francine left my office telling herself: *"This return to my old habits is normal; I'm going to take myself in hand, continue to speak positively to myself and soon everything will be fine."*

The next day, she was prepared to accept her boss' disapproval even though it hurts her. She couldn't make it disappear; she could only continue to do her best.

To Follow

The following ten chapters will allow you to recognize yourself in the experiences of others, to identify your thinking regarding various aspects of your life and give you the specific means to program yourself positively.

Personal Journal
to
Help You Control Your Emotions

"A New Way of Thinking."

When you realize that you've eaten more than usual and that your overeating was the result of a disappointment or some other emotional trauma, examine your behaviour as follows:

Sequence: A: an external cause
B: triggered a thought process
C: which resulted in an emotional response and overeating.

Example: A: **The outside factor that was the cause of the behaviour.**

B: **What I thought about it.**

C: **My emotional and behavioral response.**

YOUR NEW PROGRAMMING:
(to replace your old B sequence)

Repeat this message to yourself several times a day, if possible. Repeat it particularly when similar circumstances arise. Repeat it, also as part of your relaxation program. The more often you repeat it, the better it will work.

Use the other page to write out your own A-B-C sequence whenever you experience an emotional upset this week.

Personal Journal
to
Help You Control Your Emotions

A: The external event that set it off.

_____

_____

_____

_____

B: What I thought about it.

_____

_____

_____

_____

C: My subsequent feelings and behaviour.

_____

_____

_____

_____

My new way of thinking and my new programming
should be:

_____

_____

_____

_____

"Repeat" this new programming several times a day if
possible.
"Repeat" it particularly when similar circumstances arise.
"Repeat" it as part of your relaxation program.
The more you repeat it the more effective it will be.

Repetition is Programming

CHAPTER 4

IT'S NOT MY FAULT

Death

Carla has been seeing me for a few weeks about her weight problem. She's 52. It's early December. In the last little while her morale has been on the decline and her weight has been increasing. I had her take two computerized psychological tests: Bert, to check out her emotional state, motivation and living habits and Liza, to try to determine the causes of her behaviour.

The results were revealing: poor eating habits, low motivation with regard to weight loss and symptoms of depression. Liza disclossed that Carla had a normal, happy childhood but that in her adult life she had suffered a serious trauma.

Sixteen years ago, on December 23, she lost her husband in a car accident. At 34 she became a widow with eight children to raise. Even 16 years later she can't recall the event without crying.

She has never been able to deal with the loss. From that moment on, her life became a nightmare. For the first few months she lost weight, then her weight began to increase quite dramatically. She started eating to compensate for the loss of her husband. I actually believe she hasn't smiled once since the tragedy sixteen years ago. *"Why me, Doctor? I've been asking myself that question for sixteen years and I can't come up with an answer. I've asked my priest but he couldn't help me. There's simply no justice. My life has been completely destroyed."*

Carla's depression today is attributable, not to her husband's death but to herself. This may seem a harsh judgement but it's true. It is not the death itself but her prolonged reaction to it that is making her unhappy.

For sixteen years she has been telling herself it's unfair. Every day she has looked for someone to blame for her misfortune. For sixteen years she has ignored the positive aspects of her life, and there are many. Among other things, she has brought up eight fine children in spite of her difficulties.

I suggested that Carla try the **STOP** technique. There is no "why". Misfortune is simply a part of living that no one can change. We must accept death as we accept life. We have no other choice except to spend the rest of our days in complete misery.

Secondly, I suggested to Clara that she draw up a list of the successes she had achieved in recent years, particularly those related to the education of her eight children.

Finally, I told her to concentrate every day on the positive things that were going on around her. Every night before going to sleep she was to concentrate only on all the positive events of the day and programme herself positively for the next day.

Only through such methods as the **STOP** technique and positive review and programming can she hope to improve the quality of her life.

Blaming Someone

Let's call him Roger Goodtimes. He's 29 and almost one hundred pounds overweight. After a few weeks of dieting, he shows some improvement even though he still has a long way to go. Roger seems relaxed and self-confident. When I suggest Bert, he says:

"I don't much believe in those things. Besides, I know myself well and I don't think it would help."

Nevertheless, he finally agrees. The results are staggering. Roger is profoundly affected by his obesity. His self-confidence is, in reality, very low; he is suffering from several stress symptoms, and he is highly emotional with a marked need for perfection. In fact his perfectionism stops him from taking up certain activities for fear that he won't be 100% successful at them.

During the course of the interview I realize that the same holds true for his weight problem. He refuses to take advantage of the motivational tools I make available to him. His fear of failure is such that he would rather have the excuse of not having really tried rather than go all out and risk failure with nothing to fall back on.

I sense Roger's dicomfort. He feels under attack. He stops smiling and begins to talk.

"It's not my fault I'm fat. I weighed 10 pounds at birth. Everyone in my family is fat. We are all big eaters. It's all very well to try to eat less but have you ever been out with friends and tried not to eat while they stuffed their faces? I can't stay home alone all the time. And try watching T.V. without eating. Food ads are constantly flashing at you. We live in a crazy world. I don't smoke or drink, I've got to unwind somehow like everybody else."

So Roger isn't quite as happy as he thinks he is. His weight problem is causing him a lot of pain and there seems no way out because he keeps blaming someone or something else for his condition.

The way Roger feels about his situation is not realistic. His weight problem is not someone else's fault, it's his. There are contributing factors, of course. The fact that he was born into a family of big eaters explains why he picked up poor eating habits at a young age. But his overeating today is not his parents' fault. Nor can it be blamed on his friends, on television or on stress. Roger is free to choose. He decides what to put into his mouth. He can also decide to overcome his negative habits. I'm not saying it would be easy, but carrying around a hundred extra pounds is not easy either.

Roger has to realize that we can only change ourselves. We can't change our parents, our friends, television or society. But we can work wonders by changing ourselves.

Damned Money

After an absence of 4 months, 35 year old Jocelyn was back. At the time of her last visit she'd been very close to her ideal weight but since then she'd gained considerably. When I asked her why, she couldn't tell me. She really didn't know. So I had her take Liza, a computer test I designed to help determine the reasons people have difficulty losing weight.

Jocelyn was a social worker and her husband and engineer. Every aspect of her life seemed good: upbringing, family, work, social life, children. Liza revealed only one problem; financial difficulties.

"It's awful. My husband and I have worked hard for 12 years and we are no further ahead. With both our salaries we are just managing to pay the bills. Last summer we had to cancel vacation plans we'd made with a friend of ours who's a dentist. We had to make do with camping again."

"You seem to be quite badly affected by what you perceive as a lack of money."

"Damned money. When I was young, my family was well off and there was always enough money. I never had to struggle for it. Since we bought our house in the suburbs the expenses have eaten up all our savings, and with two growing children we can barely make ends meet. It's not easy to tell the kids we can't afford to give them some of the things their friends take for granted. This constant lack of money upsets me terribly. I think about it all the time. I realize now that it's on my mind no matter what I'm doing."

Jocelyn was beginning to understand why she'd gained weight following the change in her holiday plans. The frustration of not having enough money had caused her to overeat.

"I understand my behaviour of the last few months now, but it is still sickening to work twelve years and be no better off. Damned money. And I can't see any hope for a change in the near future unless we win a lottery."

If Jocelyn places her hopes for change in luck, she's likely to remain unhappy for a long time. The first thing she should do is a proper accounting of her financial situation. The biggest drain on the family resources seems to be the monthly payments related to the house. If that, in fact, turns out to be the case, then she'll have to determine whether they would be happier if they sold the house. Once the family makes a decision together, she'll have to accept it. Hers is not a money problem but simply a problem accepting that money is limited. Both husband and wife work and are well paid; all they have to do is learn how to spend within the limits of their incomes.

Jocelyn will have to come to terms with the fact that not having all the money she wants is completely normal. By telling herself every day that her financial situation is the inevitable result of her own choices, within a few weeks she'll have overcome the frustration that has been subconsciously tormenting her.

Alcohol

Pat is 40. She has a 15 year old son and a 13 year old daughter. She is overweight by about 25 pounds and she just can't seem to lose weight. She has tried every diet she's ever heard of but without success. She manages, with difficulty, to lose 4 or 5 pounds and then puts them right back on.

When I ask her why she's had so little success she has a ready answer:

"I'm a very nervous person because my husband is an alcoholic. During the week he doesn't drink and things are fine but on weekends he never stops drinking and it makes me very angry. He comes home late and I can't fall asleep until he gets in. If I complain that he didn't tell me he'd be late it turns into a huge fight. That's when I head for the fridge."

"Is your husband a violent man? Does he ever hit you when he's drinking?"

"Not at all. He only starts to yell when I complain about his behaviour. If he doesn't do something about his drinking I might have to leave him. I can't put up with it much longer."

"Does your husband's drinking cause you financial difficulties?"

"No. He gives me most of his pay and I manage our budget. In fact, outside of his drinking, we're a very close couple. During the week, when he's sober, we get along extremely well. But on weekends it's hell."

"If I understand this correctly, you have an ideal husband except on weekends when he consumes what you consider to be an excessive amount of alcohol."

"That's right."

"And when he's been drinking, his behaviour isn't great but it isn't tragic either."

"I guess he's not that bad. He never beats me and we don't want for anything but I can't stand his drinking. It really upsets me."

"You should try Al Anon (a group for people who live with alcoholics). It might help you understand and deal with your husband's behaviour."

"Isn't he the one who should be dealing with his drinking?"

Pat is unhappy because her husband, a fine man in every other way, drinks too much alcohol. She's right to wish he would stop drinking...

But for the moment her husband doesn't see it that way. In spite of his wife's wishes, he doesn't want to stop drinking right now. What can be done? Pat is so unhappy that she's considering separation. I don't think that would be the best solution at this point. Instead Pat should try to understand the situation and deal with it less emotionally. Only when she's done that should she consider another course of action.

In order to become happier Pat must examine herself and think about changing some of her own behaviour.

"I can't stand to see my husband drink, not even when he only has one. Just thinking he might be drinking upsets me."

"Do you understand that our emotional reactions are automatic and that their intensity may not correspond to the present stimulus? The simple recall of an emotionally charged situation can trigger a correspondingly intense emotional reaction."

"My father had a drinking problem too and it hurt my mother a lot. My father didn't actually drink that much but my mother used to panic at the mere thought of his drinking. She was constantly warning against the dangers of alcohol. Saturday nights

when we were kids we used to lie awake in terror knowing that our father would probably come home drunk."

What is happening is that every weekend Pat is reliving the terror of alcohol instilled in her by her mother decades earlier. In reality, the present situation is not that serious and in no way warrants the intense emotional reaction Pat is displaying. To break this habitual response, Pat has to de-program herself. She has to repeat to herself on a regular basis: *"I accept my husband's drinking: it's his choice. The effects of alcohol on my marriage are nothing to panic about."*

Pat has been successful in de-programming herself. Within three weeks her attitude has completely changed. Her husband is still drinking weekends and, although she still would prefer he didn't, she can accept it. She feels much better about herself and over the last three weeks she has been able to stick to her diet without cheating.

She has learned that to be happier she has to change herself and stop trying to change others. Once she had relaxed she was able to assess her marriage and her conclusions were unequivocal:

"My husband has a nasty habit, no doubt about it, but he also has a lot of good qualities and I love him very much. I don't think I could be nearly as happy without him."

Summary

According to psychologist Doctor Wayne Dyer, 75% of people are externally motivated. That is to say that they look outside themselves for reasons to account for their successes or for excuses to account for their failures. Yet our problems don't come from outside but from our reactions to outside stimuli. We must stop blaming others and look instead for the most positive ways of dealing with even the most difficult situations facing us. Certainly some people seem to get more than their share of hardships, but we all have the potential for getting through and benefitting from our experiences. The more difficult the situation the greater the potential for growth.

The death of a loved one is certainly one of the greatest trials one can face. It is absolutely normal to feel devastated for several weeks in such circumstances; it's also normal to feel the loss of that loved one for the rest of our lives. But It was abnormal and unhealthy for Carla, at 52 and 16 years after her husband's death, to ask herself every day why there was no justice. She was responsible for her own misery which she was nurturing in spite of all the positive life around her. We have no power over death but we can control our reactions to it.

Roger Goodtimes was full of excuses about his serious obesity: family, outings with friends, stress, T.V. advertising, the need for some outlet, etc. However, psychological tests showed Roger to be such a perfectionist that he refused to get involved in activities for fear of not being 100% successful. Roger would have liked society to change for him. Yet its's much more realistic simply to work on changing oneself. One need only set a goal and pursue it resolutely.

Lack of money is also a convenient excuse to account for our problems. Jocelyn didn't even realize that her chronic frustration over perceived financial difficulties was the source of her weight problem. In our society I would suggest that lack of money is rarely a real hardship. Most of us have enough to attend to our essential needs. The problem comes from our frequent inclination to spend more than we have. We have to learn to make choices and accept our responsibilities. Success is not measured by the contents of a person's wallet but by that person's self-esteem and ability to manage his or her own life. That kind of wealth goes way beyond material possessions.

Pat lived many unhappy years because of her husband's alcoholism.. It's a hard thing to accept but the only way she

69

could achieve a measure of happiness was to change herself. When she made an effort to do so she discovered that she was a victim of emotional responses she had inherited in childhood from her mother. She programmed herself to accept her husband's behaviour and to end the weekend battles. She broke the habit of reacting emotionally to the least hint of alcohol and was able to assess more clearly the state of her marriage. Even when we have a justifiable complaint, it's not within our power to change someone else. We can only change ourselves.

Our problems come not from without but from within. The choices are ours.

Personal Journal
to
Help You Control Your Emotions

"There's Nothing I Can Do About it".

When you realize that you've eaten more than usual and that your overeating was the result of a disappointment or some other emotional trauma, examine your behaviour as follows:

Sequence: A: an external cause
B: triggered a thought process
C: which resulted in an emotional response and overeating.

Example: A: **In spite of all my hard work and good intentions, I cheated on my diet again.**

B: **It's my spouse's fault. I get no help and there's nothing I can do about it.**

C: **I'm depressed so I eat.**

YOUR NEW PROGRAMMING:
(to replace your old B sequence)

It would be better if my spouse were supportive, but (s)he isn't. I am responsible for my own behaviour. I can succed if I want to.

Use the other page to write out your own A-B-C sequence,whenever you experience an emotional upset this week.

Personal Journal
to
Help You Control Your Emotions

A: The external event that set it off.

_____

_____

_____

_____

B: What I thought about it.

_____

_____

_____

_____

C: My subsequent feelings and behaviour.

_____

_____

_____

_____

My new way of thinking and my new programming should be:

_____

_____

_____

_____

"Repeat" this new programming several times a day if possible.
"Repeat" it particularly when similar circumstances arise.
"Repeat" it as part of your relaxation program.
The more you repeat it the more effective it will be.

Repetition is Programming

CHAPTER 5

THAT'S THE WAY I'VE ALWAYS BEEN

It's Too Late to Change Now

A few months ago at a party I ran into an old childhood friend. He has a thriving business that employs about twenty people. He has been married 14 years and he has 3 children. His life seems to be in great shape. Towards the end of the evening he asked if he could come to my office for a checkup. The following week I gave him a complete examination.

All the lab tests proved normal. On the questionnaire he admitted he took a tranquilizer every day at noon.

"When the phone is ringing constantly and clients are on my back I feel like my nerves are being twisted. So I take a tranquilizer just to get through the rest of the day. Do you think it's bad for me?"

"It's certainly bad to feel that much stress that regularly. And tranquilizers aren't the ideal solution. Eventually you'll have to

73

increase the dosage to get the same effect. You should work on controlling your stress more naturally."

He interrupts: *"There is nothing I can do about my nervousness. I've been like that ever since I went into business. It's not anything in particular, It's just that when things get hectic at the office I feel like my nerves are being scraped raw."*

I suggested that my friend try to replace the tranquilizers with intense physical exercise. He was skeptical but willing to try. He decided on racketball at lunch time.

Two weeks later I ran into him again and asked how he was doing. His answer disconcerted me.

"Racketball didn't work out very well. I played every day for a week then I quit. My work was suffering. I told you there was nothing to be done. It's just the way I've always been."

"But did you still feel the need for a pill after playing racketball?"

"Not at all. In fact I felt so calm I had the feeling I wasn't getting anything done."

"And did you in fact fall behind in your work during that week?"

"No, not really. But I felt I wasn't doing my best, that I wasn't involved enough in what was going on around me."

Many people feel that effciency and success are synonymous with stress and agitation.

My friend was used to associating success with stress. Since he wanted to be successful he would unconsciouly dismiss anything that might relieve his stress and then fall back on the excuse that he'd always been a tense person.

Before he can control his stress he has to become aware of that dynamic. When my friend realizes that he can enhance his business success by controlling the way he deals with stress, his life will become considerably easier and more pleasant. Success breeds success.

I Can't Understand Why

Last october, Simone was seeing me for a weight problem. After a month of steady progress, she began to put it back on.

"It's always the same story. I've never gotten down to my ideal weight. I've always failed in the past; I don't see how it could have been any different this time."

"Did you ever try to understand why you failed on previous occasions?"

"I've often thought about it but I've never figured it out. I am successful at my things but never at losing weight. I get very angry with myself."

Of course past failures do not automatically assure subsequent failures. In fact it is very negative to believe they do. However, it is not enough just to try again. You have to learn from your mistakes in order to avoid repeating them.

When I questionned Simone, I learned that she had felt unaccountably depressed over the previous two weeks. She had lost her motivation. On further questioning she admitted that the autum was a particularly difficult time for her.

"Did you ever have a traumatic experience at that time of the year?"

"About twenty years ago I lost my first husband and my daughter in a car accident. But that can't be it, it was to long ago. I've since remarried and I have other children."

As she thought about it Simone realized that every year in October she would have bouts of depression related to the accident that took her husband and child. That explained her behaviour of the previous two weeks. She had an automatic depressive reaction brought on by the simple fact that it was October. Then, disappointed by her apparent failure, she felt guilty and ate even more.

Now that she has understood the cause of her failure she will be able to take hold of herself and not allow the past to dictate her present behaviour. To achieve this she will have to repeat to herself every day for 21 days: "My past is behind me; I am the master of my present."

Good-For-Nothing

At 38, Mary has 3 children and enough extra weight that she wants to diet. During the medical examination I find that she has gastritis, a chronic stomach inflammation. She decides to follow a special protein diet which I recommend to alleviate her stomach problem.

In the first two weeks the results are spectacular. She loses 11 pounds and her stomach problems disappear. She is, of course, ecstatic.

The following week everything falls apart. She strays from her diet and her stomach pains return. When I ask her about it she says:

"I'm just a good-for-nothing. Always have been. I deserve everything I get."

My computerized behaviour monitor, Bert, reveals that she is very emotional, with 60 points, twice the norm, and that she lacks self-confidence, also by a factor of 2 as compared to the norm.

"The entire week was a bust. I had all kinds of problems with the kids. I couldn't get them to do anything. Maybe I wasn't firm enough. I'm scared I'm missing the boat with them, that they'll turn out bad."

Mary was extremely upset. She seemed very emotional about her children's upbringing. Liza (another computerized questionnaire), was going to help us understand why.

When Mary was only eight her mother died. She stayed

with her father until she was 15. It was hell. He drank a lot and lived a dissipated existence. At her mother's funeral he told Mary he'd never loved her and when she was 15 he threw her out, telling her: "I hate you, you're a good-for-nothing."

The following year, when she was still only 16, she became pregnant by the first man to show her any affection. Another disaster. The young man was soon gone. Her father pressured her to have an abortion but then she was admitted into hospital with pneumonia and came within a hair's breadth of dying. She was in a coma for a week and then she miscarried. Her father didn't once visit her in the hospital. Convinced that she was good for nothing and that no one loved her, she took an overdose of sleeping pills. This time she was in a coma for 2 days.

It's not hard to see why Mary is very emotional and lacks self-confidence. Bringing up her children today takes her right back to her own chilhood.

"I'm always afraid I'll repeat my father's mistakes; that's why I have a lot of trouble saying "no" to them. I'm so worried they'll turn out like me. When you've always been a good-for-nothing... I couldn't deal with another failure."

Mary's past life has been very difficult. Up until now it has shaped her personality and determined her behaviour. And it serves as a perfect excuse to forestall any change. But if she really wants to live a more satisfying life, to gain control over her emotions and to develop self-confidence, she can.

First, though, she has to de-program herself. She must reinterpret her past not as a personal failure but as a set of unfortunate circumstances of which she was a victim. When someone makes senseless and unrealistic accussations, the fact that he's your father doesn't make them any more valid. For a long time Mary believed her father when he called her a good-for-nothing but today she is capable of rejecting that accusation as baseless. She has wonderful qualities and a vast potential that has yet to be realized. The only thing wrong with her is the programming she received from her father. And there isn't a single reason why she can't change that.

To help her gain control of her emotions I recommended a relaxation and self-programming technique aimed at enhancing self-confidence contained on my cassette: **"Be thin by suggestion."**

Mary was to repeat to herself with conviction: "I'm developing more self-confidence every day. I have extraordinary potential and I want to exploit my capacities to their fullest. I have everything I need to succeed and I will succeed. I have more confidence in myself every day."

After a month of twice daily five minute repetitions the results were heartening. Bert revealed an improvement of 10 points in the area of stress and emotions and of 6 points in the area of self-confidence.

Of course negative thought patterns and reactions would still surface but by using the **STOP** technique she was able to keep them at bay and control their negative effects.

You can find the techniques of positive self-motivation in Chapter 21 of my book **"Be thin through motivation"**.

I've Failed at Everything

Michael, a 43 year old chartered accountant, has come to consult me about losing weight and related problems.

"You are my last hope, Doctor. I have even followed a diet under the supervision of another doctor, but I've put it all back on. As I read your book Be thin through motivation *I realized that I had to get beyond simply trying to deal with excess fat. But I have to tell you that at this point I don't hold out much hope of success. I've always failed at everything and I don't see how I could succeed at losing weight."*

His score on the computerized personality test, Bert, was 243. That is extremely high considering that the average is below 150. Michael proved to be highly emotional, guilt ridden and depressive. It was therefore surprising to note that the results also indicated a fairly sound personality base with a lot of self-esteem and self-confidence.

Here is what had happened: two years earlier, after 18 years of a marriage that had produced two sons, his wife confronted him, completely unexpectedly, with the following: "You've never made me happy. You're impossible to live with. I've tried for 18 years but I can't anymore. I've had three breakdowns and that's enough. I'm leaving and I'm taking the boys with me."

It was a devastating blow to Michael, particularly as it was totally unexpected. In 18 years of marriage it was the first time his wife had opened up to him. Over the years he had tried repeatedly to communicate with her but she was a very closed person and never confided in him. In time , he'd accepted her for what she was, believing his marriage was in fairly good shape. Now, faced with this virulent attack, he was completely at a loss. She made him feel that he was solely responsible for the separation because he had never been sensitive to her needs. He was overwhelmed with guilt and sank into a deep depression. He'd been a model employee but now his work deteriorated and he lost his job.

He'd been living on Unemployment Insurance for six months. He felt that, because his marriage had failed, he had failed as a human being. He could not reconcile himself to the idea of separation. He firmly believed in the principle of sticking it out for better or for worse.

The first phase of Michael's treatment was to help him see the situation more realistically.

The truth of the matter was that he was the victim, not the guilty party. His wife was the one who'd decided on the separation without discussion or even warning. He was probably not without some blame but he'd always acted in good faith; his wife had never communicated either her feelings or her expectations. Two years later he was still asking himself: "Where did I go wrong?"

At the conclusion of our first meeting I asked him to decribe in writing how he used to behave towards his wife. When we met again, two weeks later, I noted a marked improvement. He was walking more confidently, holding his head high and even smiling occasionally.

"I tried to be as objective as I could in describing how my wife and I related to each other. I think you were right, I had my faults but I always acted honestly and sincerely, I tried constantly to communicate with her; she was the one who never wanted to talk. I know I'm not a psychologist, I'm just an accountant, but I really wonder what I could have done differently. She used to criticize me for my interest in plants and for all my reading on the subject. She even found fault with my love of classical music. She thought I was strange because my interests differed from hers."

The truth was also that Michael's wife had been depressive since her adolescence and no treatment had proved effective in the long term.

Michael was beginning to see things in a more realistic alway. He acknowledged his share of the blame but he was, in fact, more victim than villain.

The second phase of his treatment could now begin; he must be made to see that one can fail in an area of one's life without becoming a failure overall. Michael has always lived up to his moral obligations. For 18 years he put up with his wife's nervous condition and her non-communication. He did it for the benefit of his marriage. A marriage that, nevertheless, ended in failure. He must not allow that failure to affect his entire life. Rather, he must use the experience to improve his life; to become a stronger person. The only

80

payoff of a negative experience is the potential it offers for learning and growth.

When I next saw Michael a month later he was working on all kinds of projects. His life was no longer governed by his past and he was mastering his future.

As he was leaving my office for the last time he said:

"It's incredible how blind you can be to what's going on day to day. There's something I never told you. My wife left me for my best friend. I could never face that until now. I think that made me feel even more inadequate."

Summary

It's essential that we not allow past events to govern our lives. The fact that we've behaved in a certain way in the past doesn't mean that we have to continue to do so.

What we must understand is that over time we have acquired ways of defending ourselves against emotional blows. Many of these defense mechanisms are developed when we are still relatively immature and inexperienced. Often we simply copy our behaviour on that of the models at hand, our parents. Once acquired and perfected, these defensive reactions become part of our nature and arise automatically every time some stimulus recalls the original emotional blow. When these reactions have become automatic we accept them as an essential part of our makeup. We find them normal and see them as being in our nature. "That's the way I am and there is nothing I can do about it."

As mature adults we must realize that these defensive behaviour patterns may no longer be adequate or appropriate. Now that we have gained experience and acquired resources, a situation that would once have elicited an automatic and perhaps an extreme response can now be dealt with in a more controlled and effective manner.

It is therefore important to identify our inappropriate

81

reactions and to change our emotional habits. One must not allow past behaviour to govern one's present life. Behaviour can and must keep pace with a person's evolving personality.

My childhood friend with the thriving business thought there was nothing to be done to control his stress. He'd always been tense and expected always to remain so. Even faced with the positive results of his experience with racketball he was reluctant to accept the possibility of his being efficient and successful without suffering from stress. His past was governing his life.

Simone couldn't understand why every October she would become depressed and despondent. In October she would subconsciously recall the tragic accidental death of her first husband and daughter some 20 years earlier. She was able to de-program the reaction by telling herself repeatedly: "My past is behind me; I am the master of my present."

Because her father had so often told her that she was good for nothing, Mary believed him and behaved accordingly to the extent of attempting suicide. The truth was quite the reverse. It was her inadequate father who was at fault. Yet for 38 years she had believed him. It was necessary for her to de-program herself and take a new look at her past, appreciating that she was not the villain but rather the victim.

Positive programming allowed her to develop the immense potential within herself. Little by little with successive achievements her self-confidence grew.

The great, in fact the only, consolation for life's tribulations is the potential they offer for growth, this is a potential we must never waste. In his forties, our chartered accountant, Michael, spent two years of his life thinking himself a failure because his wife had left him for his best friend. A single setback, even the breakup of one's marriage does not mean a failed life. On the contrary, such a failure should be seen in its potential for growth and improvement. Hopefully one day Michael will be able to say "I'm a better man today thanks to the lesson I learned from my painful experience."

The past should serve to enlighten the present, not to obscure it.

Personal Journal
to
Help You Control Your Emotions

"I've always been like that."

When you realize that you've eaten more than usual and that your overeating was the result of a disappointment or some other emotional trauma, examine your behaviour as follows:

Sequence: A: an external cause
B: triggered a thought process
C: which resulted in an emotional response and overeating.

Example: A: **My daughter is having problems with her husband and I'm worried about it.**

B: **I'm a worrier. I always have been.**

C: **When I worry, I can't help eating.**

YOUR NEW PROGRAMMING:
(to replace your old B sequence)

Up until now I've been upsetting myself worrying about others. It's time I learned to be more concerned about myself, and less about others.

Use the other page to write out your own A-B-C sequence, whenever you experience an emotional upset this week.

Personal Journal
to
Help You Control Your Emotions

A: The external event that set it off.

_____

_____

_____

_____

B: What I thought about it.

_____

_____

_____

_____

C: My subsequent feelings and behaviour.

_____

_____

_____

_____

My new way of thinking and my new programming should be:

_____

_____

_____

_____

"Repeat" this new programming several times a day if possible.

"Repeat" it particularly when similar circumstances arise.

"Repeat" it as part of your relaxation program.

The more you repeat it the more effective it will be.

Repetition is Programming

CHAPTER 6

I MUST DO MY BEST AT ALL COSTS

Making Others Happy

Joanna, 44, is a manager in a large department store. She has about 30 employees working for her. After attending a lecture I'd given, she showed up at my office. For the last 20 years she had suffered periodically from migraines and ulcers. The doctors she'd consulted had prescribed various medications which she continued to take daily. Eight pills a day, in fact. In spite of her ailments, her attitude was wonderful. She was always in a good mood and eager to please. She had a lot of energy and didn't seem at all tense.

Yet her symptoms were undeniably stress-related and I told her so. She was astounded:

"I'm very active, but I enjoy what I'm doing. None of my activities is particularly stressful. On the contrary, I take great satisfaction in all of them."

I asked:

"Would you say you're a perfectionist?"

"I'm efficient and ambitious; I have to be. But I wouldn't say I'm a perfectionist."

I had her keep a journal for the next two weeks and record the way she felt about the events of each day.

On her next visit, she had this to say:

"I'm still not convinced I'm a perfectionist but you've sure had me thinking over the past two weeks. I'm certainly very active. Here's what I do: I work 40 hours at the store where I have a staff of 30 and considerable responsibility, then I come home and attend to my husband and children, none of whom has ever done a thing around the house. Two nights a week I attend meetings of the social club of which I'm president. That part is relaxing. I don't think my social activities have anything to do with my complaints. But writing about my feelings just as they arose, I came to the realization that I'm always putting out fires. The moment someone around me isn't happy, regardless of whether or not I'm implicated, I'm right there to put out the fire."

From the age of 12, when her mother died, she found herself responsible for her 7 brothers and sisters. Her one goal was to make sure her whole family was happy. At 20 she married a man 10 years her senior. He was of a depressive nature and soon became dependent on her. She always had to be careful not to hurt his feelings and invariably it was she who was the "reasonable"one. She developed first rate firefighter instincts. She was soon behaving the same way towards her children, her co-workers and her friends; whenever someone was unhappy she felt it was her duty to solve his or her problems. Only now, at 44, was she beginning to realize that she'd spent her life putting out fires, that she felt personally responsible for the happiness of everyone around her. That impossible mission was taking its toll in the form of migraines and stomach ulcers.

In the first phase of her treatment Joanna must learn that each individual is responsible for his or her own happiness or misery. A wife can't make her husband happy against his will or vice versa. Neither can a mother force her children to be happy. Each individual is responsible for his or her own emotional reactions and relative happiness or unhappiness. Of course we can make ourselves available within reason when someone asks for help but we can't impose happiness on anyone. I truly believe that our greatest responsibility is to be happy ourselves in order to serve as an example and an inspiration to others.

In the second phase of her treatment Joanna will have to reconsider the way she schedules her time. Excessive activity can exhaust the body and deplete its resources, one must always try to live a balanced existence.

In order to budget her time judiciously she must use a day-planner. Since there are only 24 hours in a day,and we sleep 8 hours and take three meals of at least 30 minutes each, we have to budget our time realistically. In Joanna's case, she must learn to balance her time at work against her responsibilities at home and her social activities. She should immediately set aside some time reserved exclusively for herself. She's always putting out fires for everyone else but if she is not careful she can burn herself out.

It's absolutely essential for everyone's physical and emotional wellbeing to set aside regular, if possible daily periods in which to take stock, listen to music or otherwise relax. Only when we are happy can we share happiness.

Joanna has understood this, and now, when she finds herself wanting to put out a fire she tells herself she's not responsible for making others happy. She remains good natured and energetic and she's still available to those who need her. She has also joined an aerobics class which she attends twice a week without fail.

Last week her husband commented:

"I don't know what's going on, but you seem to have

changed lately. I don't know how, exactly, but it's a definite improvement.

The Fear of Disappointing

"I don't understand, Doctor, I think I'm going crazy. Last weekend I ate three chocolate covered sundaes and the weirdest thing is I don't even like them."

In order to try to understand her strange behaviour, I helped Caroline through the A- B- C sequence we saw earlier. You'll recall it's based on the reliable assumption that behaviour usually results from an emotional response.

"I really don't know why I got a craving for something I never eat. I'd just come back from a family get together. There had been about 30 of us. I'd had a pretty good time but I got annoyed at my mother for harping at me about my not bringing a date." So we'd found the A, the triggering event was her mother's harassing her about a date. Her mother's pressuring caused tension within Caroline and set off the urge to eat.

All that's missing now is the B, Caroline's thoughts about her mother's reprimands.

"I become very upset and angry with her. I feel I'm old enough to make my own decisions. But there's always another voice that says: She's right, you should listen to her; she knows what's best. You are letting your mother down."

Caroline's thinking is ambivalent. On the one hand, she wants to control her own life, but on the other hand, she wants her mother's approval. The latter instinct is the stronger.

Her mother has always been very strict, an authoritarian figure. Caroline was her first child and a disappointment from the start since she'd wanted the eldest to be a boy. At school Caroline was expected to be the brightest, the best and the prettiest. Caroline's early obesity was a second disappointment to her mother. As a child Caroline could never live up to her mother's expectations. Her mother was never satisfied and

90

constantly criticized her. The child, who saw her mother as the symbol of excellence, interpreted the situation as follows: "I must do everything in my power to avoid disappointing my mother and to achieve the level of excellence she expects in all things. If I can't do it, then I am inadequate."

If Caroline wishes to gain control of her emotions, lose weight and feel better about herself she must alter these unreasonable thought patterns.

Since her thoughts are the product of messages constantly repeated by her mother over the years, she must now use a similar method to acquire new thought patterns. She's perfectly justified in disappointing her mother since her mother's demands have always been completely absurd. No human being should have to strive to be more handsome, smarter or better than another; one should simply be oneself and fully exploit one's own potential. The world can accomodate an infinite number of handsome, smart and competent individuals. Everyone has his or her own individuality. And even if her mother's message had been different and realistic, Caroline has always retained the absolute right to make her mistakes and to disappoint her.

It might be nice to be able to go through life without ever letting anyone down, neither father, mother, employer nor friends, but of course that's impossible. There is nothing to feel guilty about; it's the other person who chooses to be disappointed.

And if Caroline were to pursue this logic she would realize that she's the one who should be disappointed.

In order to program herself in a more positive way. Caroline will frequently and for the rest of her life, to repeat to herself: "I like being me. I am unique and proud of who I am. I don't have to live up to my mother's expectations. I'm not responsible for her disappointments. I'm not perfect and that is perfectly normal." All methods of reinforcement are recommended: writing the reinforcing statements, even daily; recording them on a cassette and playing them back regularly; using relaxation and self-hypnosis techniques and repeating them to oneself in all kinds of circumstances.

Perhaps you are wondering why Caroline ate a chocolate sundae when she doesn't like them.

It was her mother's favorite, and once, when Caroline was twelve, her mother gave her one as a reward for losing weight without bothering to ask if she liked them.

Never to Cheat

Isabel has been on a weight loss program for exactly two months. She hasn't cheated in the entire time and has lost 31 pounds. A young and dynamic woman she succeeds at everything she undertakes. She works 4 days a week as a book keeper in a convalescent home where she is very much appreciated. Her house is always spotless and she's a wonderful cook. She is an involved mom who takes part in her children's activities, supports them in their sports and chairs the parents committee at the school attended by her two boys.

Her life is entirely regulated and she insists that it be so. She was brought up by rigid parents who demanded perfection and as a strong person she has always taken it upon herself to solve everyone's problems. She wasn't allowed to make mistakes and that's the way she liked it. She was prepared to understand and accept mistakes in others but not in herself.

At the very beginning of her weight loss program Isabel registered in one of my motivation and behaviour courses. Once, when I pointed out to her privately that she didn't seem at ease in the group she announced:

"I feel ashamed and mortified at not being able to solve my weight problem on my own. I took your course to be sure of succeeding but it's a serious blow to my pride."

She admitted that she had told no one she was on a diet and said that when she was with people she would eat more, even though she would have to starve herself later, simply to hide the fact that she was dieting.

Up to that point Isabel' s weight loss program had gone very well. She was attending class regularly and doing all the assigned work and exercises. She was the ideal patient.

The following week, everything fell apart. For the first time in two months the scale didn't register any loss; indeed it indicated an increase of one pound. She couldn't deal with this at all. She was devastated and extremely upset with herself. She was being so hard on herself that she couldn't even entertain the possibility of a logical explanation for her cheating or that she could turn it into a learning experience.

With persistent questioning I finally learned that in addition to her usual busy schedule she'd had to attend to her mother who'd fallen and injured her hip that week. She had gone to the hospital every day and helped out her father who was home alone.

She'd raced around all week and had had little time to prepare proper meals.

While the quantity and quality of the food she had eaten had not been great for her diet, they hadn't been sufficiently bad to cause significant weight gain either. In fact stress itself causes water retention that can easily account for an extra two pounds. So, in spite of the circumstances, she'd probably actually lost about a pound of fat. She was only partly relieved when she left my office. Isabel is an exteme perfectionist. Everything is either perfect or disastrous. She takes on enormous responsibilities and expects 100% performance from herself. It's good to be ambitious and to want to succeed but it's very harmful to be unable to accept the occasional failure or setback, and taking on too great a load can also be harmful. The frantic desire always to do too much too well is inevitably exhausting. Isabel is still young and her body is able to deal with the wear and tear but it will catch up with her eventually. When she has worn out her reserves, various symptoms will show up all at once and it will be too late.

Isabel takes pride in succeeding at everything, she undertakes and can't understand why she has a weight problem. In reality, it's the stress related to her quest for perfection in everything she takes on that drives her to overeating.

To program herself positively I suggested she repeat: "I'm allowed to cheat but not to give up. I can only progress by learning from my mistakes."

Since Isabel is also extremely active, I recommended she keep a detailed daily diary. As far as I know Wonder Woman is a fictional character.

Do you know what she said when she left my office? Looking at the graph I provide my patients to monitor their progress, she said:

"I hope, later, you'll erase this entry from my record."

The Quest For Excellence

Peter, 32, works for the telephone company. He's come to consult me about chest spasms and fatigue. He wanted clinical tests and X-rays right off. I decided to examine him myself and interviewed him about his symptoms first. Afterwards, I gave him my diagnosis: his symptoms were due to stress related nervous tension.

The important thing now was to identify the cause of the situation. He told me his problems had started some 5 months earlier. He had always worked outside maintaining the company's equipment and he'd gotten along very well. In fact, he had done so well he was promoted and put in charge of 6 employees. From then on, however, he had to work behind a desk.

I continued my assessment, *"In my opinion you're a perfectionist. That's probably what's causing your stress and the related symptoms."*

"I don't know if I could be called a perfectionist but I do strive for excellence. I'm responsible for 6 employees and if I don't set an example, the whole department will fall behind."

"I can't disagree there. Certainly working hard and working well are worthwhile goals. But doing one's best is different from expecting to achieve perfection and refusing to accept any shortcomings."

"But, no matter how hard I try, I still can't do my new job competently. It's been 5 months now and I don't think I'll ever get it right."

"What does your supervisor think?"

"I met with my boss just last week and he said he was pleased with my work, but I'm not. My desk is littered with files that need attention and I feel like I'll never get through them all."

Peter's case is typical. He'll never be able to control his emotional difficulties nor his stress until he learns to see things differently.

The first step then is to learn to accept, by frequent daily repetitions, the idea that:"I always do my best but I'm prepared to accept that I can't do the impossible." It is impossible to be perfect all the time.

The next step will consist in eliminating the negative ideas he holds about his work performance. Understimating oneself is a grave fault. Instead of focusing on his failures he would do well to concentrate on his successes. The fact that his superior is happy with his work should be a source of motivation and enthusiasm. Setbacks are to be expected and should serve to spur us on to greater success. Peter has great potential for success but he doesn't want to wait for experience. Yet experience, by definition, takes time. By imposing unrealistic expectations on himself he's being his own worst enemy. His health won't hold up under the pressure he's putting on himself. The **STOP** technique will be very useful at the beginning to help him get rid of the negative ideas he has about his job performance.

The third step in his treatment will be to plan his work more efficiently. First he'll have to clear up his desk. Nothing is more nerve wracking than to feel buried under a pile of paper work. All his files should be put away, preferably out of sight.

Next, he will have to budget his time. A day-planner is an invaluable tool. Taking into account the fact that he has only two hands, two feet and one head, that there are only 24 hours in a day and that he only spends 8 of them at work, he'll have to order his files according to priority. Each day, he'll have to assign himself a manageable number of things to do. Once he has planned his work in a reasonable fashion, if he still can't deal with everything expected of him by his superiors, he'll have to try to get them to reconsider the goals and objectives of his job.

"My boss said he'd get me help if I couldn't handle it but up 'till now I felt that asking would be a sign of incompetence."

Many people have told me that their superiors are not as understanding as they might have wished and that they feared for their jobs. Indeed many managers do pressure their employees to produce, but as a rule they value conscientious workers and would prefer not to lose them. However, should it ever come down to a choice, I think it's better to lose a job than to lose one's health.

The fourth step will be for Peter to build periods into his day during which he can unwind, exercise or just take stock. These will serve to make him all the more efficient at his work.

The fifth step will be proper nutrition. Because he's been overworked, Peter has taken to skipping meals or eating poor quality fast foods. A badly nourished, out of shape body provides little energy to the brain.

To reduce stress, he will also have to make sure he gets 7 or

8 hours sleep.

Peter's comment: *"I'll never have time to do all that."*

"Time isn't something one has, it's something one takes. In any case, if you don't take the time now to attend to your health, you'll have to take even more time later to attend to your illness."

Summary

A perfectionist might describe himself as follows: even at the risk of completely exhausting myself I must always do everything in my power to succeed, and if I fail, I must be held accountable. Perfectionism is a serious character flaw that frustrates normal human achievements.

Usually people agree with that last statement when it refers to others. We can understand that no one should exhaust himself or herself at a task, that no one can be perfect in all things and that no one should feel guilty if his or her efforts are not met with absolute success. And yet we often don't adopt the same reasonable attitude when it comes to ourselves. A large number of people can't accept the fact that they aren't perfect, they exhaust themselves trying to be and feel guilty when they don't succeed.

The values we learned from our parents, our schools and our churches must be at the source of these attitudes. I feel people should try to do their best, and I believe the happiest of human beings is one who strives for self-improvement, but I don't think anyone has the right to drive herself or himself to exhaustion in pursuit of any goal, particularly since we often set unrealistic ones, nor to feel guilty for falling short.

A perfectionist can display one of two types of behaviour: striving to the point of exhaustion and thereby creating debilitation and sometimes fatal stress, or total paralysis. In the case of the latter, he or she refuses to undertake anything for fear of failing. Such a refusal is the only unforgivable error I know of. Any other error provides a learning opportunity but if one does nothing, no progress is possible.

Recognizing these things is one thing, living by them is another. The only way I know to get rid of perfectionism is to live through an anxiety and guilt producing situation. Only through our negative experiences can we become conscious of how we see ourselves. Then, paper and pencil in hand, we can write down the A B C sequence of our behaviour, if we follow that process, our mistakes will necessarily become learning experiences. It's the exact opposite of guilt and self punishment. Only by analysing our mistakes can we truly introduce a new psychology of happiness into our lives.

Once we've clearly identified our thoughts about the event we can then re-program ourselves by frequent repetition of the more realistic thinking we wish to acquire.

At 44, Joanna, the store manager, realized that she'd made a mission of trying to make everyone around her happy. She'd spent her life putting out fires to the point of neglecting her own needs. In budgeting our time, it's good to set some time aside for helping others but it's also essential to reserve some for ourselves. It's a necessary condition for a well balanced personality. Let's remember that we can't be reponsible for the happiness of others. Each individual is responsible for his or her own happiness.

From a very early age Caroline had been programmed by her mother to be other than who she really was. She was torn between her reluctance to disappoint her mother, the desire to be perfect and the need, at 30, finally to be herself. Since programming that goes back to early childhood tends to be tenacious, it requires vigorous de-programming techniques. She had to tell herself constantly: "I am not responsible for my mother's nor for anyone else's disappointments."

Isabel, perfect in nearly every way, was embarrassed at not being able to deal with her weight problem alone. Yet it was the very stress created by her frantic quest for perfection that led her to overeat. She had to learn from her mistakes. The week she cheated provided a perfect opportunity to recognize that she was a normal human being and that she had to accept herself as such. Unfortunately, she didn't seem to benefit from that opportunity. She was more concerned with having the extra pounds struck from her record.

Peter, 32, would never have considered himself a perfectionist with regard to his new responsibilities and his 6 employees. But, in fact, he was pursuing excellence to the detriment of his nerves and general well being. Now he is programming himself by frequently repeating: "I'm doing the best I can, I can't expect to do the impossible." He must also begin to value his successes and to make sure he relaxes and restores his body since it provides energy to the brain.

One of the most essential yet underrated tools for stress free efficiency is the day-planner. It must be realistic and provide for periods of rest or relaxation. This reduces stress and maximizes efficiency. A woman comes to my office. She's extremely upset. She feels oppresssed and can't manage to relax even with the techniques I suggest to her. Upon questioning, I learn that in addition to her housework, this mother of 3 must help her husband who has just started a confection business. Their basement is overflowing with the candy products and she's responsible for packaging. She has become overwhelmed and unable to function.

When I helped her fill in her day-planner, we calculated the number of hours required for housework. Taking into account her hours of sleep, time for meals and a half hour a day for herself, we concluded that she couldn't devote more than four hours a day to packaging candies. Then we calculated the time it took to fill one bag 3 minutes. She could therefore easily fill 20 bags an hour, 80 a day. Since her husband's needs were greater than that, it became obvious that she required help.

The following week she was radiant. Her stress was gone.

Her husband had hired her sister-in-law to assist her and together they'd had no trouble meeting the demand. Surprisingly, once she had relaxed she was able to fill not 20 but 30 bags an hour without stress.

Get rid of perfectionist notions. Learn from your mistakes, it's the only way to progress. Get rid of guilt, it's all in your head anyway. Never mind the opinion of others, you are responsible only to yourself. Those who would judge you probably make more mistakes than you do since judging others is in itself a serious mistake.

Personal Journal
to
Help You Control Your Emotions

"I've Never Had
Any
Success In The Past."

When you realize that you've eaten more than usual and that your overeating was the result of a disappointment or some other emotional trauma, examine your behaviour as follows:

Sequence: A: an external cause

B: triggered a thought process

C:which resulted in an emtional response and overeating.

Example: A: **Someone told me I wouldn't be able to maintain my low weight.**

B: **Twice in the past I've lost and then regained a lot of weight. She's right. I won't be any more succesful this time.**

C: **I lost heart and ate.**

YOUR NEW PROGRAMMING:
(to replace your old B sequence)

My past failures can help me succeed this time. I won't repeat my errors.

Use the other page to write out your own A-B-C sequence,whenever you experience an emotional upset this week.

Personal Journal
to
Help You Control Your Emotions

A: The external event that set it off.

_____

_____

_____

_____

B: What I thought about it.

_____

_____

_____

_____

C: My subsequent feelings and behaviour.

_____

_____

_____

_____

My new way of thinking and my new programming should be:

_____

_____

_____

_____

"Repeat" this new programming several times a day if possible.
"Repeat" it particularly when similar circumstances arise.
"Repeat" it as part of your relaxation program.
The more you repeat it the more effective it will be.

Repetition is Programming

CHAPTER 7

WHY ME?

What If It Happens To Me?

"I didn't sleep a wink," Erica is explaining. *"I'm extremely upset. Imagine! I heard on the news yesterday about a man who killed his wife and son and then turned the gun on himself. It's horrible, and what's worse is that it happened in the very town where I was born, I even think I might have known their parents. Anyway, I didn't get a minute's sleep. Why do these things always happen to me?"*

Erica worries about everything that goes on around her. She spends her days looking for horrible things that might happen to her and, of course, she finds them. She listens religiously to news reports and reads the gossip magazines daily to find out what misfortunes might have befallen her favorite stars. She gets choked up reading Dear Abby.

"Don't laugh, Doctor. A person can't be too careful. All these misfortunes could happen to me or my children. Like last week I

*read about a rock star who died of a drug overdose. Well, I lay
awake for two nights until my son got back from a weekend at a
friend's cottage. It's not easy being a mother."*

"Does your son take drugs?"

*"Of course not, but you never know. Someone could slip him
something without his knowing. All kinds of things happen. For
example, take my niece and her husband, they both died in a car
accident last year. I couldn't get out of bed for a week. You can't
be too careful with everything that goes on these days."*

When I suggested she do relaxation exercises and repeat
positive statements to herself to reduce her stress, she said"
*"How can you expect me to be calm and relaxed with all the hor-
rible things that go on today? I think I was meant to bear a heavy
load. There's nothing you can do about my nerves. Don't even
try."*

The stress and emotional turmoil Erica goes through are
not the result of the events themselves but of the way she
thinks about them. Her thought pattern might be summarized as follows: life is full of terrible negative things and
since I have no luck there's a good chance they'll happen to
me.

That's precisely the kind of unrealistic thinking she has
to change if she wants to improve herself. In order to do that
she has to start avoiding the negative as much as possible. I
advised her to stop listening to news reports which are usually negative. To stop concentrating on the misfortunes of
others and never again to read a lonely hearts column. She
has to stop seeking out misery and instead look for happiness. And, surprising as it may seem, there are more positive
than negative things in the world if only you look for them.

I also advised her to read books on self improvement and
motivation as well as the biographies of successful people.

Finally, I advised her to practice the **STOP** technique to
arrest all negative thoughts and to concentrate on all the

positive things in life: a fine husband, two healthy, intelligent children, money enough to satisfy her needs, a comfortable home and the physical ability to undertake anything she wants to.

In reality the potential for happiness was all there in her life but she couldn't see it for her unrealistic fear of misfortune.

She was the creator of her own misery.

Misfortune Dogs My Days

Linda, fifty year old mother of a 25 year old son and a 19 year old daugther, had been seeing me for a few weeks about a weight problem.

"I'm pretty tired of having to eat the same bland things all the time. I can't wait to go off my diet" she said.

"What are you eating?"

"Steak, steak, steak, lettuce, lettuce, lettuce and more lettuce. I'm turning into a rabbit."

"Indeed, that is a rather monotonous diet, but you're allowed a variety of foods. You should make the effort to prepare interesting meals, that way you won't become frustrated. You enjoy seafood. Why not look up new, delicious seafood recipes that are compatible with your diet?" I gave her a list of appropriate recipe books.

"I don't think it would work. I feel that if it tastes good. it can't be slimming."

Poor Linda actually believed that you have to be miserable and frustrated to lose weight. She went on:

"Anyway, a week doesn't go by without something dreadful happening. Misfortune follows me everywhere. It hangs on like a bad cold."

"What, for example?"

"It's awful, my son and his wife were separated last week and they have a darling two year old daughter. They made such a fine little family! There's always something. I'll never enjoy a moment's peace in my life."

When she found out about her son's separation, Linda ate for a solid week.

"It's too bad about your son's separation, but you'll have to learn to react positively or else you'll end up with two problems instead of one. Your blood sugar level is much too high and if you don't drop your excess weight you could end up with some serious complications."

"I'm really not very lucky. I have only the one son and he's separated."

"Do you feel guilty?"

"No, I've always done everything I could for him. But I can't deal with the failure of his marriage."

"Your son is a separated person from you. You can't nor should you try to live his life. He is solely responsible for his actions, good or bad. You can be disappointed about his separation but your priority must be your own life."

"That's easy for you to say. You don't have the problem I have. I hope for your sake you never do..."

"You know, everyone has his own problems but their seriousness varies with the way they're perceived. How's your son dealing with his new situation?"

"He doesn't seem to be too upset. He even says he feels relieved; things had become so tense between him and his wife. I think he's less upset than I am."

Linda feels it's normal to live her son's life vicariously; she feels his failures as her own. This sort of thinking is unrealistic. Even a mother can't live her children's lives for them. Her first duty is to be as comfortable and happy as possible within herself in order to share her happiness and provide a positive example. Right now particularly, her son could use a mother who is positive rather than one who is depressed.

To achieve this state of mind, Linda will have to use the **STOP** technique and repeat to herself: *"My children choose what they feel is best for them. That's their responsibility. Mine is to be as happy as I can possibly be. They can work out their own problems."*

It will be an uphill battle. As she was leaving my office, she said:

"Anyway, there isn't much point in following your weight loss plan. Everyone I know who lost weight on a diet put it right back on. And with my luck I'm sure...."

"STOP. You're falling back into your negative, wrong minded ideas. If you look only for the negative you'll find it, but if you stop taking on other people's problems and look for happiness intead, then happiness is what you'll find."

Summary

Many people feel it's normal and may even consider it their duty to experience vicariously the problems of others. Such an attitude is neither morally laudable nor otherwise justifiable. Indeed, morality requires that we seek our own happiness and that, as creatures of the Divine, we reflect that happiness of which the Divine is the ultimate paradigm.

It is perfectly normal to feel sad when someone close to us seems to be having problems but destroying ourselves by taking on the emotional burden and stress of another is perverse. We were created to be happy; misfortune only plagues those who constantly seek it out.

At 44, Erica had always looked for misfortune in the lives of others and was unhappy herself thinking those same misfortunes could as easily be hers. She found what she was looking for even though life had dealt her all she needed in order to be happy. She had to put a **STOP** to news reports, gossip sheets, soap operas and lonely hearts columns. Even though the potential for happiness was all around her, she was looking elsewhere for misfortune.

At 50, Linda felt that misfortune dogged her days. Others were fortunate; they had no problems; she had them all. She felt her son's separation was a personal failure, and her negative feelings about it were more intense even than her son's. Under the circumstances, her son didn't need a depressed mother but rather one who was happy and optimistic. Neither her son's separation nor her difficulties losing weight are terrible misfortunes exclusive to her. They are typical of life's negative events, unpleasant enough in themselves that they require no exaggeration. In fact, since we can't control them, we would do well to try to find what is positive about them.

It's not true that misfortune constantly befalls the same people; it is just that some people constantly seek it out.

Personal Journal
to
Help You Control Your Emotions
"It's unfair.."

When you realize that you've eaten more than usual and that your overeating was the result of a disappointment or some other emotional trauma, examine your behaviour as follows:

Sequence: A: an external cause
B: triggered a thought process
C:which resulted in an emotional response and overeating.

Example: A: **At a dinner party, a friend, who's as skinny as a bean pole, ate four times as much as me.**
B: **It's unfair. I have to deprive myself while others can eat as much as they want with total impudence.**
C: **I felt cheated, so I ate.**

YOUR NEW PROGRAMMING:
(to replace your old B sequence)

I eat according to my own needs and metabolism. There's nothing unfair in that. We all have our own problems.

Use the other page to write out your own A-B-C sequence,whenever you experience an emotional upset this week.

Personal Journal
to
Help You Control Your Emotions

A: The external event that set it off.

_____
_____
_____
_____

B: What I thought about it.

_____
_____
_____
_____

C: My subsequent feelings and behaviour.

_____
_____
_____
_____

My new way of thinking and my new programming should be:

_____
_____
_____
_____

"Repeat" this new programming several times a day if possible.
"Repeat" it particularly when similar circumstances arise.
"Repeat" it as part of your relaxation program.
The more you repeat it the more effective it will be.

Repetition is Programming

CHAPTER 8

TO BE ASSERTIVE
OR
NOT TO BE

I Am Not Afraid To Say What I Think

Thirty-seven year old Sam, a participant in one of my behaviour and motivation classes, was telling me about an experience of his:

"I coach a hockey team at the local arena. I volunteer several hours of my time every week to help out the kids. Last week I had a disagreement with one of my players' father. The boy is one of the best on the team and his father wanted him to get more ice time. He took his complaint to the league manager who's a good friend of his. I was told to comply with the father's wishes and that the league manager himself would be behind the bench to make sure I did."

"I took action immediately. I wrote him a 3 page letter telling him exactly how I felt about him and the league directors. I said they were acting like a bunch of schoolboys and offered them my resignation."

Sam had been hurt, he'd reacted impulsively and his diet had gone by the boards all week. And even though he loved coaching, he'd now resigned from it.

"I love working with kids: I'm going to miss it a lot. But I couldn't take the league manager's decision lying down."

"I understand that you were hurt and I think you are probably right in this instance but you may not have used the best means to express your feelings and ideas. As a result, you'll be deprived of doing something you enjoy because of someone else's wrong behaviour. It might have been possible to face up to this person and express your feelings in such a way that you wouldn't have had to resign."

Sam was due to meet with the league committee three days later. I suggested he use the **DESC** method to help resolve his problem.

DESC stands for:

D = describe the situation

E = express your feelings about it

S = specify what you would like to see changed

C = consequences: -positive if the situation is resolved.
$\qquad$ -negative if the situation is not resolved.

It is essential, particularly when you first start using this techique, to write everything down before you meet the other party involved in the conflict. Each statement should be short, direct and free of exaggeration.

Sam prepared his **DESC**.

D-The situation is that you imposed your decision without hearing my side and you want to keep an eye on me from behind the bench.

E- I felt hurt and felt I'd been treated like a child.

S- I'd like us to be able to communicate better without

112

your spying on me.

C- If we can come to an agreement on these points, the atmosphere will be much more pleasant and the kids will benefit. I feel I've proved my worth in the past. If we can't come to some agreement I'll have no choice but to resign.

As you see, Sam's **DESC** is short and to the point. In describing the situation you have to stick to the single most important issue. Other details can be resolved later.

In describing your feelings you have to be honest and non-threatening.

In outlining the changes you'd like to see, be realistic and lay out only one at a time. You can't expect a person to alter all of his behaviour overnight. You have to put yourself in the other person's shoes and ask yourself what can, in reality, be expected at this point. It might also be helpful to express what you are prepared to change, before you make your demands on the other party.

In laying out the consequences, you should highlight the positive results for both parties. You should also hint at the negative consequences of an opposite decision. However, it's important not to exaggerate these out of proportion.

Sam went to the meeting called to review his case.

"Everybody was tense when I arrived. After my letter, they were all expecting me to be on the offensive. I started out by shaking hands with each of them, looking them straight in the eye and smiling. Then I laid out my DESC just as I'd practiced it at home. As I spoke I could see their faces change. At first they didn't know quite what I was up to, then they began to relax and soon they too were smiling. When I was through with my DESC the league manager got up and said he was sorry if his actions had hurt me. That hadn't been his intention. As for the conflict, he admitted he should have consulted me but said that he'd avoided it because of my cantankerous reputation."

Sam won his case. He continued to coach and his relations with the others involved improved considerably. He learned how to express his feelings and ideas in a non-threatening manner and he earned the respect of his colleagues. In gaining control of his volatile emotions, he had made great strides.

My Children Don't Listen To Me

Helen, a 38 year old single parent, showed up at my office discouraged, depressed and completely drained. She worked hard as a bank teller 36 hours a week. At the same time she had to bring up a 10 year old boy and a 14 year old girl.

"I'm at the end of my rope. The children don't listen to me anymore, they don't help around the house, they don't even make their beds. They want more and more money and they make me feel like a bad mom if I can't give it to them. They hardly ever study and my daughter badgered me until I let her go to the local dance and stay out until midnight on Saturday night; I'm fed up and I spent the whole week eating."

If I was going to help Helen we had to define the situation clearly.

First of all she admitted she'd always spoiled her children on the grounds that they had no father at home and that, in any case, they'd have to face life's hardships soon enough. The children had grown accustomed to getting their own way all the time. They'd come to believe that, since their mother gave them whatever they demanded, making demands was appropriate behaviour. They would have to be completely reprogrammed.

You can't program children 10 and 14 as you would a child of 5.

I asked her: *"How do you try to get them to cooperate with you?"*

"Like anybody else, I just ask them to do the things I feel they should be doing. But it's no use. Even when I yell and threaten them, they still don't listen."

When children become adolescents, they're a little like adults, they don't like to take orders. They're trying to assert their own identity and autonomy. In their awkward attempts to do so, they are often likely to do the opposite of what's requested of them.

I suggested to Helen that she prepare a written **DESC**. Here's what she came up with:

D - She described the situation in the house as follows: you're no longer children; you want to be treated as young adults and you're right. We're all full members of our family unit. Yet you're doing little or nothing to ensure the proper functioning of our home. You don't make your beds, clean up your rooms or participate in the household chores. You're not even attending to your primary responsiblity, your school work.

E - Here's how she described her feelings: I'm exhausted and at my wits' end. I can't keep doing everything around the house all by myself...

S- She expressed the specific changes she would like to see in this way: since we're all in this together, I would like all of us to participate in determining individual responsibilities.

C - She saw the consequences as follows: If we can define and respect certain responsibilities, I'll be very relieved; I'll have more energy and I'll be in a better frame of mind. I'm also prepared to give you an allowance to commensurate with the work you do. On the other hand, if you don't want to accept any responsibilities, I'll have to cut off your allowance, ground you on weekends and cancel camp for next summer.

Helen gave them each a copy and waited to see how they'd react.

The next day, as soon as she saw her, her 14 year old said: "Heavy letter mom. What do you have in mind?" Helen was thrilled. Mom and her two kids got together and worked out their new responsibilities.

Overnight the situation changed. The children felt involved, things were no longer being imposed on them; they'd participated in the decision-making themselves. They were learning responsibility. And they appreciated the rewards.

Everything didn't suddenly become perfect. The mom occasionally had to cut off an allowance. But on the whole, things ran smoothly and she didn't have to resort to severe punishment.

Some people might object to giving children a financial reward. But rewards are a part of human behaviour. It's one of the reasons we repeat behaviour that is considered good. The reward must first and foremost be verbal. It's important for Helen to congratulate and express her appreciation to her children when they display a positive attitude. A word of appreciation is invaluable.

In addition, a financial reward, when it's deserved, helps the child feel more responsible for himself and helps him or her learn the value of money.

Punishment has fallen into disrepute in our society. Reward and encouragement are certainly more positive ways of instilling proper behaviour. Nevertheless, punishment remains a valid way of discouraging inappropriate behaviour. However, the threat of punishment if it is never applied is of no use. Also, like a reward, a punishment must be in keeping with the act to which it is a response.

Because Helen properly applied the DESC method, she wasn't driven, as was a woman in Salt Lake City, to go on strike against her children. Having failed completely to enlist the cooperation of her three children 6, 8 and 9, she went on a total strike: no more housework; no more meals. After three days the children caved in and offered her a contract. Here's how she summarized the situation: *"I think the best way to get the little boy is to treat him like a man and we all know the quickest way to a man's heart is through his stomach. I'm very happy I stuck to my guns."*

All Men Are Selfish

Catherine has been trying in vain to lose weight for a few weeks. She seems very tense.

Suddenly she blurts out:

"All men are selfish. For twenty years I've devoted my life to my husband and he doesn't give a damn about me. He doesn't think about whether or not I'd like to have sex with him. Whenever he's ready, he expects me to be ready too. I've never turned him down. I've always tried to satisfy his every desire. He's never cared about mine."

"Finally, the other night, I'd had enough. After picking on me all evening, his highness decided he wanted to make love. It seemed I wasn't good for much else but I'd do for that, I went off like a bomb. I told him there was no way, and that, in any case, I'd never climaxed in the twenty years of our marriage."

"I had blurted it out before I could stop myself. I think I was more stunned than he was. He stood there for a minute, then he left the room. We haven't spoken since. I spent the week eating. I don't know what to do anymore. I'm sorry I said what I did, but it's too late."

"I think you're justified in your complaints and right in your demands, but you might have chosen the wrong time and place to assert yourself. You probably first should have talked about what was wrong twenty years ago."

117

"But I loved my husband and I thought that in time he'd come to understand. Ironically, I didn't want to hurt him and now look what I've done to him. Is there anything I can do?"

"Does your husband love you?"

"I don't know anymore after what I said to him..."

I told Catherine I'd get in touch with her husband to ascertain the extent of the damage.

When I met with him, a week later, his attitude surprised me. He was defeated and depressed. *"Your call was very timely. In fact I was just about to call you. The fight the other night was our first in twenty years and I haven't been the same man since. I can't sleep anymore; I can barely get my work done; I'm always exhausted and I can't concentrate. And I can't be mad at my wife; she must have suffered terribly all those years. I'm mad at myself for not having seen it."*

Catherine's husband had always thought their life together was perfectly normal. His parents had had the same kind of relationship and his mother had never complained. Nor, in the 20 years, had his wife so he'd always thought she was content.

He said: *"I love my wife and I've spoiled everything."*

Here was a couple who loved each other but whose lack of communication had almost destroyed their marriage. Catherine was as much to blame as her husband. She should have asserted herself and expressed her legitimate needs right from the start. As for him. He should have been more sensitive and responsive.

When I'd reviewed the situation I asked each of them to prepare a DESC, expressing his and her own feelings, taking care not to go on the attack.

To maintain dialogue, I suggested they plan to spend time together, just the two of them, preferably outside the home, at least once a week for the rest of their lives together.

118

When I last heard from them, they'd joined a sexology class and they were behaving like young lovers.

Being In Company Can Be Hard

Linda had lost a lot of weight on a special protein diet and she was very pleased with herself. On one of her weekly visits she said:*"I'm very anxious about this coming weekend. My husband wants me to go to a party with him. It'll be my first time out in the two months since I started my diet."*

"Why didn't you go out in all that time?"

"I turned down all invitations while I was dieting because when I'm in company I have a tendency to cheat."

"I'would encourage you to go out and meet people. Meeting people is one of life's pleasures. It's hard enough depriving yourself of the food you enjoy, there is no sense making it worse by also depriving yourself of the company of people who like you. If you do, you'll become extremely frustrated and as soon as you go off your diet you may be tempted to compensate with a binge."

"You're probably right, but I can't control myself when I'm in a group. I'm afraid everything will fall apart on the weekend and I won't be able to regain control. That's how I failed last time."

"I have some understanding of your fear but the best cure for fear is action. Concentrate on the upcoming party and tell yourself you'll be in control. Imagine the situations you'll be in and feel the inner satisfaction of turning down the food you don't want to eat. If you want to develop positive behaviour, you have to start with a positive attitude. Don't forget that success isn't measured against perfection. Even if you can't achieve perfection, you'll have made some progress in controlling your behaviour in groups. Even a 5 or 10 percent improvement over your previous behaviour amounts to success. The next day you'll feel good about yourself and you'll go back to your diet with renewed resolve. Go out with your husband and enjoy the evening."

The following week, Linda didn't show up for her appointment.

Two weeks later she told me: *"I almost gave it all up. I tried repeating messages to myself but that didn't work. People congratulated me for losing weight, said I looked younger, then tried to get me to eat as much as they did. Somehow it made me feel uncomfortable and the more uncomfortable I felt the more I ate. The worst of it is I wasn't even hungry; I had to force it down. Afterwards I felt so guilty I had nightmares all night. I woke up in a cold sweat from a dream in which giant cookies shaped like faces had chastised and humiliated me in front of all my friends. During the following week I often considered giving it all up but I kept thinking of one of the things you'd said to me: you're entitled to cheat but not to give up."*

In the discussions that followed we established that Linda was driven to eat not by her taste for food but because she was unable to refuse it when it was offered, particularly in a group situation. She was afraid that she would offend the person doing the offering and be rejected.

In group conversations or discussions she would never express her feelings or her thoughts if she felt they might offend even a single person in the group. She sought approval and appreciation from others at any price. She experienced a keen sense of personal defeat and felt diminished if anyone seemed to think negatively about her.

Linda's inability to assert herself in a group is a serious problem that compounds her difficulties with weight control and that could lead to negative feelings and a loss of self-esteem.

Nobody can be liked by everybody, it's absolutely impossible. Our first duty is to be ourselves and develop our own qualities. That doesn't mean we should go around alienating everyone. Indeed we should do our best to maintain good relations with as many people as possible. But not at the cost of negating our own personalities. When you negate your own personality, there is no one left for others to appreciate.

Each of us is unique and each of us must work at developing his or her own unique personality. This implies, of course, that we must respect the uniqueness of the other person as well. In general, people like someone who is original and stands out from the crowd, provided that person also recognizes the originality of others.

So, Linda should begin to express her ideas and feelings; I suggested that she begin by preparing her first victory, either with a small group or with a single individual, perhaps her husband, her brother or sister or a friend.

The second step was to learn to refuse food she didn't want, even in company. To help her achieve this, I taught her the parrot technique.

This technique requires that you constantly repeat the same word or phrase until the person who is being insistent is worn down. For example she could practice repeating to a volunteer or into a tape recorder: "No thank you, I don't want any". In a real situation, if the insistent person comes back 5 times or even more, you just repeat the same thing with a firm attitude, a smile and no further explanation.

People expect you to cave in, but once they get the idea that you mean what you say, they'll stop harassing you.

At her next visit, Linda recalled; *"I had my sister and brother-in-law over and I was finally able to turn down food I didn't want in spite of my brother-in-law's insistence. It's great! I've never been more proud of myself! Your parrot technique actually works. But you are right, you have to practice and get used to hearing yourself say the words out loud."*

Summary

Most of the negative feelings a person has, come from his or her difficulties in relating to others. Lack of self determination or poor presentation are often to blame.

As long as Sam was afraid to tell people what he thought, he reaped what he sowed: aggressiveness. Because of his vindictive attitude towards the league manager, even if he was right, he almost gave up an activity he enjoyed and believed in.

To assert oneself does not mean to attack others and point out their faults. There are effective ways of resolving interpersonal conflicts to the greater satisfaction of both parties. The **DESC** technique, for example, is a good problem-solving tool.

Thirty eight years old, single parent, Helen managed to enlist the cooperation of her two spoiled children by writing them a **DESC**. Rather than blaming them, she pointed out that they had become young adults and that it was time they assumed responsibilities and reaped rewards appropriate for their ages. I think one of the greatest gifts we can bestow on children is a sense of responsibility. And to help them acquire it, parents must be prepared to assert themselves. Giving them too much without asking anything in return or stifling them with too much authority will impair their growth since they won't develop a sense of responsibility for their own actions.

Catherine's 20 years of self-effacement almost destroyed her marriage. A successful union requires honest self-assertion on the part of both spouses. We must never take for granted that the other knows what we are thinking or how we feel if we have never spoken about it. We mustn't say "If it were me, I'd understand, so my partner should as well."

It is our duty, then, to clearly express our feelings, thoughts and expectations and to repeat them whenever our partner seems to have forgotten. By the same token we must also be open to what our partner has to say. It is in this respect for diversity where each defends his or her own point of view while accepting to consider the other's that the most successful unions are founded. When they finally learned to communicate, Catherine and her husband were like young lovers again.

Because of her inability to assert herself in a group, Linda was in the process of destroying her health and her self-esteem. Her entire life was oriented not toward her own growth and development but towards gaining the approval of others. She was afraid to turn down food for fear of offending people. She denied her own personality to avoid sanction. She began to recover by repeating to herself daily: "I'm the most important person in my life and I must love myself if I want others truly to appreciate me". Then she practiced the parrot technique to develop the ability to refuse.

Here are a few pointers for those who need to learn to refuse:

1. Say "no" from the start and dispel any ambiguities.
2. Don't try to justify yourself.
3. Be honest, direct, firm and express yourself clearly.
4. Practice refusing. Imagine a situation and record the requests and your refusals on tape.

To end this all important chapter on interpersonal conflicts, I'd like to offer you a clear outline of what should be done and what should be avoided in preparing a DESC. The DESC technique is extraordinary and I recommend it highly. It can dramatically improve your relationships. It works almost like magic and sometimes surprisingly fast.

1. Begin by thinking about the conflict situation.

2. **Then in writing,**
   - Describe the situation
   - Express your feelings about it
   - Specify what you want out of it and the
   - Consequences (positive or negative).

3. Here are the dos and don'ts for a positive **DESC**:

	DO	**DON'T**
D E S C R I B E	D1 Describe the behaviour of others objectively	Describe your emotional reaction to their behaviour
	D2 Use concrete terms	Use vague abstractions
	D3 Describe the time, place and frequency of the behaviour	Generalize with terms like "always".
	D4 Describe the action, not the motivation	Try to imagine someone else's motives and goals.

	DO	**DON'T**
E X P R E S S	E1 Express your feelings.	Deny your feelings.
	E2 Express yourself calmly.	Indulge in emotional outbursts.
	E3 Express your feelings positively & relate them to your goal.	Express your feelings negatively & aggressively.
	E4 Address the specific behaviour, not the entire person.	Attack the character of the person involved.

	DO	**DON'T**
S P E C I F Y	S1 Ask for a specific change in the other.	Ask for a general change.
	S2 Ask for a limited change.	Ask for too great a change.
	S3 Ask for only one or two changes at once.	Ask for too many changes at a time.
	S4 Specify the behaviour you'd like to see end & that which you'd like to replace it.	Ask for non specific changes.
	S5 Make sure your request doesn't entail too great a loss for the other party.	Ignore the other party's needs & think only of yourself.

		DO	DON'T
	S6	Specify the behaviour you'd be willing to change.	Think only the other party should change.

DO   DON'T

C		DO	DON'T
C O N S E Q U E N C E S	C1	Be explicit about the consequences.	Avoid mentioning rewards and pusnishments.
	C2	Reward positive change.	Only punish the refusal to change.
	C3	Choose something in the interest of the other party.	Choose something interesting to you only.
	C4	Choose a reward motivating enough to sustain the positive change.	Offer a reward beyond your ability to produce.
	C5	Choose a punishment suited to the behaviour	Make exaggerated threats.
	C6	Choose a punishment you can follow up on.	Make unrealistic threats or choose defeatist punishments.

4. DESC summary

The more practice you have, of course, the better you'll become at it. Eventually, you may not always have to write the whole thing down. In some situations you might even be able to come up with an appropriate **DESC** spontaneously without writing anything down.

5. Mail or telephone **DESC**:
Very useful in certain situations. Always meet face to face if possible.

6. Write down your **DESC** only when you are calm, relaxed and you've thought things out.

Personal Journal
to
Help You Control Your Emotions
"I Am Obese."

When you realize that you've eaten more than usual and that your overeating was the result of a disappointment or some other emotional trauma, examine your behaviour as follows:

Sequence: A: an external cause

B: triggered a thought process

C: which resulted in an emtional response and overeating.

Example: A: **Someone asked me if I'd put on more weight recently.**

B: **I don't like anyone to talk about my obesity.**

C: **I got angry, snapped at the person and ate more than usual.**

YOUR NEW PROGRAMMING:
(to replace your old B sequence)

It would be better if people were more diplomatic, but if they're not, that's their problem. I know I have a weight problem and I'm dealing with it.

Use the other page to write out your own A-B-C sequence whenever you experience an emotional upset this week.

Personal Journal
to
Help You Control Your Emotions

A: The external event that set it off.

_____

_____

_____

_____

B: What I thought about it.

_____

_____

_____

_____

C: My subsequent feelings and behaviour.

_____

_____

_____

_____

My new way of thinking and my new programming should be:

_____

_____

_____

_____

"Repeat" this new programming several times a day if possible.
"Repeat" it particularly when similar circumstances arise.
"Repeat" it as part of your relaxation program.
The more you repeat it the more effective it will be.

CHAPTER 9

THE WORST THING THAT COULD POSSIBLY HAPPEN

A Thief Robbed

Suzanne has come to my office in desperation. She can barely speak; she's short of breath; her hands are shaking and she hasn't slept for 4 days.

"I've gone completely to pieces since I got back from my vacation. My house was broken into while I was away. It's terrible; it's simply awful; I just can't deal with it. They took all my jewelry, my stereo and my television set."

Suzanne is in a panic. She sees the robbery as a total disaster.

"You can't trust anyone these days. Everybody's a thief."

She seems to be badly overreacting to a simple break-in. It's as though she had lost more than just a few material goods.

I ask her to analyze the specific act that has caused her to panic, the break-in, and to tell me the "terrible" consequences she seems so concerned about.

"I'll have to advise my insurance company. The police have already been by and they're supposed to be back to take down the details of everything that was stolen. I'm scared to walk into my house now. I'm afraid there'll be somebody in there taking the place apart and I'll come face to face with him."

To save time I asked Suzanne to take the Bert computer test so we could get a clearer overall picture of her personality and emotional state. The results showed she was highly emotional, 63 as compared to an average reading of below 30, and that she had a marked tendency to overdramatize.

"You're absolutely right. That 's me to a "T". That's a real crystal ball you've got there. I'm scared of every little thing. I'm a nervous passenger in a car; I never talk to anyone I don't know; I try to avoid taking the subway specially at rush hour....and I'm scared of thieves. I can't help it, I always fear the worst."

"How long have you been this emotional?"

After a second she said:

"I lost my only daughter 10 years ago. She died of a brain tumor. A year later my husband drowned while on a fishing trip. Before that, I was easy going and nothing bothered me. You've helped me see something I'd never thought of before, Doctor."

"Now I understand more clearly. You're upset not just about the loss of your jewelry, but more significantly, about the loss of your daughter and husband, which the theft brought back to the surface of your consciousness."

"I think you're right. I'd never thought about it in those terms but now that you mention it, the image I have of the loss of daughter and husband is one of theft. I've always felt the two people most dear to me were stolen away from me."

"I think it's time to de-program yourself because, in effect, you've been your own worst thief over the last ten years, stealing all
130

of life's precious moments from yourself."

The first step required Suzanne to break the habit of associating all of life's incoveniences with a tragedy. When you see misfortune everywhere you end up courting it. I told her to begin writing down, on the spot, every incident that stirred up negative feelings in her and to record, as well, the worst and best scenarios the incident could give rise to. Having brought the incident down to realistic proportions Suzanne was to ask herself: "Is the incident, in itself, so terrible?"

She was then to use the **STOP** technique every time she felt negative emotions coming on and to repeat to herself 20 times a day: "I've stolen enough from my life as it is, I must put a stop to it."

The results were startling. After three months Bert recorded an amazing 25 points improvement. Suzanne was ecstatic:

"For the first time in ten years I feel I can breathe freely. I've broken out of my prison."

What If It's Cancer

At 59, Loretta was diabetic and overweight. Her family doctor had referred her to me to help her lose weight but, with a standard 1200 calorie diet, she'd had no success.

We agreed to put her on a special 500 calorie diet supplemented with protein and I advised her to stop taking her diabetes medication since, at 500 calories, her blood sugar level would be controlled by diet alone.

I explained to her that according to the best medical information available to-day, the only valid treatment for diabetes in obese people is weight loss. 80% of overweight adult diabetics would no longer be diabetic if they could maintain their ideal weight. Unfortunately, most medications used in the treatment of diabetes, because of their chemical action, prevent or make weight loss more difficult.

Armed with this information, Loretta enthusiastically undertook her diet. Within the first month she'd lost 11 pounds and her blood sugar level had fallen from 240 to 120, the norm being at 115. She was delighted and felt younger than she had in years. A few days later, however, I received an urgent phone call from her.

"I've had severe heartburn since yesterday and I have a lump in my stomach. I've lost a lot of weight over the past month; I'm sure I've got cancer." She was literally in a panic.

After questioning her about what she'd done and what she'd eaten over the previous few days, I concluded that she had gastritis.

"You have a stomach irritation due to excess acidity. Your weight loss is due to the diet you've been on for the past month and you don't have to worry about cancer." I suggested she take an antacid, avoid acidic foods and come see me in a few days.

I hadn't seen Loretta for several weeks when I ran into her general practitioner.

She'd gone to see him convinced that she had stomach cancer. For the second time in 5 years he'd had her undergo all the appropriate diagnostic tests: X rays, ultra sound and even a gastroscopy (a fiber-optic probe that allows the examiner to view the inside of the stomach). All the results proved negative.

"I've known her for 10 years and it's always the same story. At the least sign of discomfort she thinks she has cancer. I worry about patients like that. Too often I've seen them develop cancer, apparently as a result of constantly thinking about it."

You can, in fact, become what you pretend to be. During the last world war, the draft was in force. In order to get out of it, some men read up on the symptoms of various diseases and practiced simulating them convincingly. Ironically, many of them ended up contracting the very disease they had feigned. Loretta is already sick, not with cancer but with the fear of cancer. It's much more common, lasts much longer and can be as devastating as the real thing.

I was recently talking with a 32 year old father of two who had struggled with leukemia. He told me: *"It's the best thing that could have happened to me. I'm not afraid anymore, I have learned to take each day as it comes and to savour the experiences it has to offer. Every day is the most important day of my life and I live it as though it were my last. I don't let trivial cares spoil it."*

It's too bad we have to come close to dying before we learn to appreciate our most precious gift. Loretta will have to overcome her obsession because fear has never nurtured health. Every time a negative thought comes into her mind she should divert it with the **STOP** technique and turn her attention to an imagined scene in which she is happily and heathily involved in an activity she loves and that she can enjoy now and for many years to come. That way she can program her conscious and subconscious mind with positive health goals and dispel her negative fear of disease.

Who Does He Think He Is?

A while ago my wife and I were at a party when we ran into a friend of my wife's whom we hadn't seen in many years. Let's call her Angie. She was about 46, slightly overweight (maybe 15 pounds) and wore a lovely low-cut dress. The evening was going alone fine when Angie's brother-in-law, slightly tipsy, commented to her: "Your dress is great. A little tight in all the right places. You look terrific."

Angie's face dropped, she looked daggers at her brother-in-law and then headed straight for the hors-d'oeuvre table. She began to eat as though she hadn't eaten in two days, my wife went up to her.

"Who does he think he is?" Angie said between mouthfuls.

"Telling me I'm too fat. I'm not going to stand for it. Did you see the beer belly on him?"

She was upset and angry and couldn't stop eating. My wife tried to calm her down. It was no use. In the end she spoiled her whole evening and probably put on a pound or two in the process.

A common problem that often brings on negative feelings is misinterpreting what others have said.

Some people automatically look for put-downs in everything that is said to them. They always expect the worst.

Angie immediately assumed her brother-in-law's comments were a dig about her weight, whereas they might well have been an awkward compliment about her figure.

In considering a situation that has given rise to negative feelings it's often helpful to look at the two alternatives: the worst and the best. Even if her brother-in-law really had meant to comment on her weight, how should she have reacted? All that can be said is that he is neither blind nor particularly well mannered. It's not always advisable to speak the truth. But I don't think Angie had any reason to be upset. If she isn't happy with her weight it should have served as an incentive to diet. If she feels comfortable the way she is, she shouldn't pay any attention to him. Whether you are fat, thin or otherwise there will always be someone who'll find something negative to say. You can never please everybody.

Every day we're constantly confronted with people and events that are unpleasant but since we do not have any control over them, the best we can do is accept them philosophically. Their words in themselves can't hurt, only the way we choose to interpret them.

Here's a key statement you should repeat hundreds of times, particularly in unpleasant situations: **IT WOULD BE BETTER IF PEOPLE AND THINGS WERE DIFFERENT, BUT**

THEY HAVE EVERY RIGHT TO BE AS THEY ARE.

Angie should have said to herself: "It would have been better if my brother-in-law had been more tactful, but he has every right to say all the dumb things he wants to say."

We can't change people and we can't anticipate everything they're going to do or say. Whatever we can't change we should simply accept. It doesn't mean we have to agree with everything. **IT WOULD BE BETTER ... BUT...**

It's a magic statement that will spare you a lot of negative feelings. Repeat it often and it will become a habit, useful in all kinds of situations.

It's not fair

"It's just not fair. My husband worked for the same company for 32 years and now he's lost his job. All those years he worked for a starvation wage, then they give him the gate. There's just no justice." Jane is 48 and she is very upset. Her husband who is 50 has just fallen victim to a plant closure. At his age he has little chance of finding another job.

"I recommend that you spend time, immediately, analyzing the situation as cold headedly as possible, then imagine the worst and the best consequences."

"You can't tell me there's anything fair in his losing his job at 50. At his age, he'll never find another one."

Basically she's right: life isn't fair. That is the way of the world. The sparrow eats the worm and the spider eats the fly. Floods, droughts, volcanos, earthquakes and tropical storms aren't fair. People are not all born equal. Some are tall, some short, some crippled and some impaired. Jane is right, there is no justice and there never will be. Her only mistake is not accepting that. Even though there is no justice, she's free to make choices with regard to her own happiness.

I suggested: *"The worst possible scenario you can imagine is*

135

still not a tragedy. Your husband will collect social security benefits for a while, you're working and you only have one child left at home. I understand that it WOULD HAVE BEEN BETTER for your husband to have kept his job BUT he had no choice in the matter. And even if worse comes to worst, your situation does not appear desperate."

"I never stopped working all my life except to raise the kids and now I'm going to have to keep on. That's really unfair. I've got a right to a little rest too. God knows I've earned it."

As I interviewed her, I learned she had always been sensitive to injustice; she'd fought it constantly, especially in the work place, even in situations where she wasn't personally involved. And more often than not it had cost her. When I had her take the computer questionnaire we call Liza, I found she'd been particularly affected by her father's second marriage.

"I was 12 when my father remarried and I could never deal with it; I always felt he'd been stolen from me."

That was the beginning of her sensitivity towards injustice. To help deprogram herself she would have to reinterpret her father's remarriage as, not an injustice towards her, but the normal behaviour of a 35 year old widower. Although at twelve it might well have been hard to accept, today she should be able to see it as normal.

"It's amazing that we can feel or behave in a certain way for 35 years without ever understanding why. Today I realise that my father was absolutely justified and I'm no longer angry with him at all."

Now she will have to lose the habit of automatically reacting every time she perceives something as being unfair. After every negative experience she should write down and repeat to herself: *"It would be better if there were no injustices in the world but there always will be and there is nothing I can do to change that; I just have to accept it."*

When I last heard from Jane she was making great strides in dealing with her negative emotions. She was doing the repeating exercise regularly and she was very happy with her progress.

She admitted: "*You'll remember, I didn't want to consider the possibility of any positive outcome to my husband's losing his job. Well, I was wrong. My husband is happier than he's ever been. He's found a part time job as a park attendant and he loves kids.*"

Summary

One of the most common causes of negative emotions is dramatizing—ascribing an exaggerated importance to certain things or events.

According to some psychological research, up to 92% of the worries people have are unnecessary; 40% are about things that will never materialize, 30% have already happened and 22% can't be avoided. Thus in 92% of cases we worry for nothing, and, on top of that, we tend to exaggerate our legitimate worries. We make mountains out of mole hills.

I remember a statement by internationally renown psychologist, Denis Waitley: "One of the best ways of adapting to life's difficulties is simply to accept them as normal. From the moment we begin to see them as occasions for positive change, adversity and misfortune begin to make us proof against the negative effects of stress."

Because of her fear of being robbed, Suzanne had become her own worst thief. The deaths of her daughter and her husband had triggered an emotional shock that remained a part of her for several years. But human beings have the wonderful ability to deprogram themselves of the false and unrealistic ideas poisoning their lives.

She practiced the STOP technique and repeated to herself: IT WOULD HAVE BEEN BETTER if I hadn't been robbed, BUT I've lost enough as it is, I'm certainly not going to continue robbing myself.

59 years old Loretta's morbid fear of cancer was, in itself, a worse affliction than the disease itself. We become what we fear. An obsessive fear of illness has never engendered health. Negative always breeds negative. Her exaggerated fear of cancer, her diabetes and her obesity are destroying her and she's doing nothing to help herself. She should put a **STOP** to her fear and program herself with images of health and interesting activities.

In my 14 years as a doctor I've often noticed that it's not illness that perturbes patients the most but rather the fear of illness. Yesterday I met one of my closest friends, a 40 year old colleague. 6 weeks ago he suffered a heart attack, a coronary thrombosis. I asked him what kind of nervous state he'd been in while it was happening (he'd identified the symptoms during a tennis match). He said he hadn't been nervous at all; his only thought had been to get to the hospital as quickly as possible. When he got to emergency he nearly went under and he heard a nurse say she could barely get a pulse.

"At the time I realized I might die, but it's amazing how relaxed I was." And, of course, the story has a happy ending.

Angie was hurt by her brother-in-law's insinuations about her figure. She gave his comments a meaning that was probably never intended. She saw them as an insult but why not give them the opposite interpretation? If she'd taken the remark as an awkward compliment, her evening would not have been spoiled. She's the one who chose to feel hurt.

Unfortunately, we can't alter what other people say. We can't stop them from saying things that are hurtful or untrue. But we can change our attitude towards what is said to us. We can say **IT WOULD BE BETTER IF** people were otherwise **BUT** they have every right to be as they are.

Jane has always decried injustice. It upsets her terribly. She mortgaged her own happiness to fight injustices she could not possibly make right. She wouldn't see the positive things that can be drawn from life's setbacks, she preferred to rage against unfairness. Everyone knows there's no justice in the world. People are sick, poor, hungry, criminalized and victimized in a thousand different ways. The only justice I know of is to take ourselves in hand and work at being as happy as possible. Happiness is contagious. You can't share something you don't have to begin with.

Jane's secret formula was: "IT WOULD BE BETTER IF there were no injustices on earth BUT there always will be and I must learn to accept what I can't change."

Personal Journal
to
Help You Control Your Emotions

"What's The Worst
Thing
That Can Happen?"

When you realize that you've eaten more than usual and that your overeating was the result of a disappointment or some other emotional trauma, examine your behaviour as follows:

Sequence: A: an external cause
            B: triggered a thought process
            C:which resulted in an emotional response and overeating.

Example: A: **The union is considering calling a strike.**
           B: **It would be terrible. It would eat up all our savings.**
           C: **I'm anxious, so I'm eating.**

YOUR NEW PROGRAMMING:
(to replace your old B sequence)

Nothing ever happens exactly as I expect. Anyway, I'm going to take things one day at a time, and I'll take care of problems as they arise.

Use the oder page to write out your own A-B-C sequence,whenever you experience an emotional upset this week.

Personal Journal
to
Help You Control Your Emotions

A: The external event that set it off.

_____

_____

_____

_____

B: What I thought about it.

_____

_____

_____

_____

C: My subsequent feelings and behaviour.

_____

_____

_____

_____

My new way of thinking and my new programming should be:

_____

_____

_____

_____

"Repeat" this new programming several times a day if possible.
"Repeat" it particularly when similar circumstances arise.
"Repeat" it as part of your relaxation program.
The more you repeat it the more effective it will be.

Repetition is Programming

CHAPTER 10

THERE ARE SOME THINGS THAT CAN BE DONE AND OTHERS THAT CAN'T

Everything In Its Place

I met 60 years old Andy on an international flight. We were seated next to each other so I couldn't help noticing his excessive smoking and, hearing him cough, I suggested he should give it up as his lungs obviously could no longer take it.

"Are you a doctor?" When I said I was, he replied: *"You're right, of course, but I can't stop. If you have some magic method I'd like to hear about it."*

"Why do you think you smoke so much?"

"Because I'm under a great deal of stress. I'm in business and it's not easy to please all your customers, nor is it always easy to deal with labour. And let's not forget the government: they are always thinking up new ways to gouge you. I tried to quit but within two days I was going nuts so I started again."

We ended up talking for several hours. He'd done very

143

well in business and he attributed his success to the lessons he'd learned from his father. One of the things he had been taught at a very young age was that there was a place for everything and everything belonged in its place. His father had been very authoritarian. When he said dinner would be at 6:05 he didn't mean at 6:04 nor 6:06; rules had to be obeyed.

At 12, Andy was as mischievous as the next boy, and to discipline him, his father sent him to a boarding school. That was his first emotional shock.

For the first six months he was rebellious and constantly challenged the school authorities. Then he thought of taking a new tack. "Since I'm here and there is nothing I can do about it, I may as well get the most I can out of it." He soon became a model student. He was granted the appropriate privileges and was made a school monitor."

"I learned that you could profit from following the rules."

From then on he worked hard to make sure things went according to the rules and that everything was kept in its place. He became scrupulously punctual, so much so, that whenever he had to be somewhere he allowed ample time for the possibility of unexpected delays. If he was held up in traffic he would get furious with himself if he hadn't made sufficient allowance. He would go to any lengths to please others, never thinking of himself. In business, if he caused someone else to lose a small amount of money he would be devastated, whereas if he himself lost 3 or 4 times as much he would shrug it off. Andy had rules and principles and everything had to be in its place.

One day he suffered a second emotional shock. While he thought that his family life was going along just fine, his wife advised him through a lawyer that she wanted a divorce. Her grounds were his paternalism.

"It was never clear about how she meant that. I thought about it for months." he said.

144

One of the definitions of paternalism is : "A system under which an authority undertakes to ...regulate the conduct of those under its control..."

What Andy had been doing, without even realizing it, was imposing his own rules on people, believing, as he had learned, that that was the only way to be happy and successful.

His spouse had failed to understand that he did it, not to dominate her, but to try to make a good life for her.

A few years later he suffered a third emotional shock: a perforated stomach ulcer.

"I came within a hair's breadth of dying. I was even given the last rite."

"I suppose the fear of dying you experienced at that time is at the bottom of the stress you're feeling even today."

"I wasn't afraid of death. When I felt myself going, I saw a white light at the end of a dark tunnel. I felt very relaxed. Death no longer frightens me. I feel it will be a positive experience."

"How do you explain your constant everyday stress?"

"That, I don't know. I was hoping you could tell me."

His stress was not caused by a fear of death but rather by a fear of living a less than perfect life. He was afraid things would not all fall into place in his life and he was exhausting himself trying to achieve an impossible goal. This obsession his father had imposed upon him was even more powerful than the thought of death.

"It's too bad we didn't meet 20 years ago. Maybe then I could have gotten rid of the compulsion that has caused me so much stress." he said.

"There's no magic solution, but you should start right now to talk to yourself in a positive way. You should repeat as often as possible: it would be better if everything were always in its proper

place, but it's impossible and perhaps that's just as well."

All One Way or The Other

When Sharon came into my office, she was extremely disconcerted. Her voice was weak when she said: "I don't know what's the matter with me. I ate like a pig all week: cheese cake, pies, maple syrup..."

"There must be some reason for your binge."

"No more than usual, I can't think of anything outstanding that happened this week."

"When you took Bert (a computerized psychological test) last week, I found that you were very emotional and that can cause a binge. However, there must be some emotional shock, a disappointment or a frustration that sets off the response. If you ever hope to change your eating habits, you have to find it. Otherwise the binges will just keep recurring. Monitor your feelings this week by keeping a journal and try to figure out what happened last week."

The following week we discussed her journal.

"I don't know whether it has anything to do with my binge last week, but I remembered that I'd never gotten a call I was expecting from a boyfriend who was supposed to discuss weekend plans with me. I was very resentful, particularly since I then had a boring weekend. As I was writing my journal I discovered that I was always all one way or the other. I'll be very strict with myself and very disciplined, then all of a sudden I'll relax completely. I either starve myself or binge all out. I see a lot of guys all at the same time or none at all. I save every penny or I splurge. That's the way I am. Moderation is just not in my nature."

"How were your parents with you when you were growing up?"

"Well, about a month ago my dad was sick. Believe it or not, I was glad. He brought so much suffering into my life. I was glad it was his turn. He was very hard on us. If bedtime was 7:00 o'clock, we had to be in bed at 7:00 o'clock sharp. He would never relent under any circumstances no matter how hard we pleaded. I was
146

very afraid of my father. He'd been in the army in the last war and he imposed military style discipline. At school my sister and I always had to be first or else we'd be beaten."

Sharon had come to resent her father for his excessive discipline. On the one hand, she was programmed to follow orders and do her best. While on the other, she needed to rebel in order to preserve her own personality. That's why her behaviour is so changeable and goes from one extreme to the other.

Before she can overcome her excessive eating she has to deal with her feelings. In order to control her feelings she'll have to change the way she sees things. For example, she'll have to understand that it would have been better if her friend had called her but that he had every right not to.

Finally she'll have to learn that between two extremes there is a balance point. Otherwise she'll keep falling into the same trap as her father. She'll have to tell herself repeatedly: *"I accept that things, people and situations are not always black or white, positive or negative, perfect or disastrous."*

For starters, I suggested she follow a balanced diet of 1200 calories per day, one that wasn't too strict; then I suggested she balance her budget and that she might want to try one boyfriend at a time.

As she achieves some success, she'll come to realize that she can behave in a balanced, moderated fashion. And success will breed success.

If Only Everyone Felt As I Do

I'd been seeing Gertrude about her weight problem for a few weeks. At 38, she was the mother of a 17 year old daughter. She was in a rage at her daughter.

"It's terrible. Kids today have no taste. She's always wearing jeans and some outrageous top. You should see the colors! It's

frustrating. You try to help them develop a little taste but it's no use."

Having been frustrated all week, Gertrude had blown her diet. She went on:

"When I talk to my husband about it he just says it's her choice, that I should let her go ahead. You'd think he agrees with her."

"I'm having trouble understanding why you're so upset over what seems to me a rather trivial matter; your daughter's lack of taste in clothes."

"She never listens to me. I don't think she has any respect for me as her mother. When I was growing up we never would have considered defying our parents, not even at 21. Some things have to be respected or else you have anarchy and chaos."

Gertrude has her set ideas and she stands up for them. For instance she believes men and women have different roles in society. *"It's normal,"* she says, *"That's the way it's always been. The woman cleans the house, does the laundry, prepares meals and brings up the children. The man goes out to work, brings home the money, takes out the garbage and does the heavy work around the house."*

All of a sudden she asks:

"Don't you agree, Doctor? If everyone saw it that way we'd have a lot less trouble."

"You may be right. I don't know. What's right for today isn't necessary right for tomorrow. What's right for one individual is not necessarily right for another. What is important is not whether or not you're right but whether the way you see things makes you happy. And it seems to me you haven't been too happy this week."

"What do you mean, doctor?"

"I don't doubt that you believe firmly in your priciples and that they're true for you, but even if you are right, you have to agree that

148

your daughter, your husband or anyone else have the right to see things differently. You must admit that your daughter was probably happier than you were this past week."

"Probably..."

"If you ever hope to control your emotions you must learn never to say that people should do this or that; rather, you should say: why should I bother about what they do; it's their choice; they're the ones who have to live with it."

She interrupted me: *"Easter's next week and I warned you right from the start that I'd cheat then. Easter without chocolate just isn't Easter.... You understand, don't you, Doctor?"*

Gertrude was equally convinced that Christmas without a Christmas cake just wasn't Christmas, that St. Valentines's Day required a chocolate heart and every birthday, a cake.

"I understand you have your customs and habits, madam, all of them supported by the confection industry, but it's a good thing your daughter doesn't always see things your way or she'd have a weight problem too!"

You Can't Trust Anybody

At 42, Phillip owns three woman's wear stores. He has 38 employees.

He's overweight, has high blood pressure, is extremely tense and looks 55. His wife brought him in to see me so I might help get him back into shape.

After examining him, I recommend a special protein diet to get his weight down quickly and bring his blood pressure under control. I also recommend a 5 minute per day relaxation program on cassette:"Be thin by suggestion", and a 20 minute, three times a week, exercise program. The important thing for him is not to try to do everything over night, but slowly to regain control over his physical condition.

He says:

"You're right, I should take better care of my health. But with 38 employees, I'm under terrible stress; I don't even know if I'll be able to stick to my diet."

"The reason you have to relax, exercise and eat properly is precisely that you need it. If you ever want to enjoy the money you're making, you have no choice. Otherwise, you might be rich but all you money will go to treating your ill health."

"The problem is I've got to do everything myself. Every time I delegate responsibility I end up regretting it. I expect things to turn out perfectly and they never do. Having employees is no picnic these days."

"I understand that an employee may not be as enthusiastic or efficient as you are, but overall, can't you delegate some responsibility without opening the way to disaster?"

His wife piped in:

"He's always been that way. He's never been satisfied with anyone else's work. He thinks he's the only one who ever gets things right. And that doesn't just apply to his business. We had the car fixed last week and he hassled the mechanic for overlooking some detail. When our house was being built a couple of years ago, the contractor almost quit over my husband's constant harassment. And don't ever go shopping with him; you think women are fussy shoppers, you haven't seen anything till you've seen him in a store. He's always got something to say. If the product is good, the service was lousy; if the service was good, there was something wrong with the merchandise."

Phillip not only expects a lot from others, he increases his own stress every time they fall short of his standards. By constantly finding fault and criticizing he's only punishing himself. Stress affects his blood pressure and his eating habits and it causes him to age prematurely.

"Do you think your employees are capable of being perfect?"

"Ultimately, I know they can't be. It's crazy. I behave as if they

could be and it's killing me..."

"Realization does not immediately change habitual behaviour. You'll have to repeat to yourself several times every day: people don't have to be other than who they are. They don't have to try to be perfect. It's up to me to adapt to who they are."

"You think that's going to make a difference?"

"Absolutely. But It's not going to work overnight. In any case perfect results don't exist and shouldn't be expected. For the next while it will be extremely difficult for you. As soon as you have reason to be disappointed you'll be inclined, automatically, to criticize as you always have. You have to expect that. But that's when you should practice repeating to yourself that people need not be different from who they are. If you do that on a regular basis, I promise you'll see a very positive change in your outlook and behaviour within 3 weeks."

"You figure it'll work in just 21 days?"

"I sure do, as long as you do it every time. And remember, if you don't take the time to get your health back now, you'll have to spend at least as much time dealing with illness later."

I saw him again a month later. He'd lost 16 pounds and his blood pressure was down to normal.

"I talk to myself every day, Doctor. And it's working; I've never felt better. I'm planning my work more efficiently and delegating responsibilities to my employees according to their abilities. And I don't expect them to be perfect all the time. Whenever there are problems, I just tell myself they're to be expected in any business and I am surprised and pleased when there aren't any. My stress level is way down and I'm thinking of opening another store."

"Don't forget to take the time to deal with your health."

"Don't worry, Doc. I'm working out three times a week and doing relaxation exercises at least as often. And I find I have even more time for work now. I'm not about to give that up, I assure you."

Summary

You should always guard against absolutes, obligations, rules and imperatives. Whether they come from society, your parents, your spouse or yourself, you have to become free of them if you wish to be well.

Andy, a successful 60 year old businessman, had been programmed by his father to believe that everything must be in its rightful place. For the rest of his life he exhausted himself and suffered considerable stress trying to live up to this ideal which he'd made his own. That obsession accounted for his divorce and for his perforated ulcer. His commitment to rigid rules set up a stress in him greater than the fear of death.

Sharon was brought up so strictly by her father that she was torn between his military style commands and the need to assert her own individual personality. This dichotomy set up a pattern of extreme behaviour. She either starved herself or went on a binge ; she saw either no one or several men at once; she saved every penny or squandered her money. To break the pattern she had to practice balanced behaviour and learn to control her emotions by accepting what she couldn't change and by programming herself for moderation.

At 38 and with a 17 year old daughter, Gertrude will have to learn to moderate her views as well. She is entitled to her way of seeing things but she must learn to accept that others have that privilege too. It's never a question of who's right and who's wrong. She'll have to learn to free herself from absolute judgments on herself and others.

At 42, Phillip looked 55. He was overweight, had high blood pressure and was constantly under stress because he expected too much from others. He was his own worst enemy. Within a month his health and the quality of his life improved dramatically. He learned to talk to himself, followed my diet and started doing physical and relaxation exercises.

He found time to take care of his health, and time enough, as well, to open another store!

Personal Journal
to
Help You Control Your Emotions
"It's Terrible."

When you realize that you've eaten more than usual and that your overeating was the result of a disappointment or some other emotional trauma, examine your behaviour as follows:

Sequence: A: an external cause
B: triggered a thought process
C:which resulted in an emotional response and overeating.

Example: A: **I suggested something to my child and he did the opposite.**
B: **I find it terrible and unbearable when my children ignore my advice. I was right.**
C: **I felt frustrated and ate too much.**

YOUR NEW PROGRAMMING:
(to replace your old B sequence)

It would be better if my children listened to me all the time, but they have the right to make some of their own decisions even if they end up in trouble. It's not terrible and shouldn't seem unbearable; it's just natural.

Use the other page to write out your own A-B-C sequence whenever you experience an emotional upset this week.

Personal Journal
to
Help You Control Your Emotions

A: The external event that set it off.

_____

_____

_____

_____

B: What I thought about it.

_____

_____

_____

_____

C: My subsequent feelings and behaviour.

_____

_____

_____

_____

**My new way of thinking and my new programming
should be:**

_____

_____

_____

_____

"Repeat" this new programming several times a day if
possible.
"Repeat" it particularly when similar circumstances arise.
"Repeat" it as part of your relaxation program.
The more you repeat it the more effective it will be.

Repetition is Programming

CHAPTER 11

I FEEL GUILTY

I'm A Closet Cheat

"I just don't understand myself," Frances is saying. *"Last weekend I went to a sugaring off party and didn't stray from my diet once. My friends and family never stopped badgering me: "You've lost enough weight; you don't know what you're missing. It's so good; come on, you only go around once." They tried everything but I held on. I didn't give in, and I've never been more pleased with myself."*

I interject:

"You know people are often bothered by the fact that someone else is eating properly and losing weight. They feel envious, jealous or guilty. They might wonder: "What's she got that I haven't got? How come she can manage to lose weight?" They might also be thinking: "If I can't prove that her weight loss is only temporary, I'll be shown up as being inadequate! "So they do everything in their power to try to make sure the other person puts on weight just to

157

prove they aren't inadequate. It's important to understand the reactions and behaviour of the people around you as you can deal with them appropriately."

"This time they weren't the ones who got me," she interrupts. *"I got myself. When I came home, I waited until my husband had gone to bed, then I snuck to the refrigerator, took out half a cake and literally went into the closet to eat it."*

She waits for my reaction, expecting the worst. I say nothing; she continues:

"When other people are around, I'm strong, but when I'm alone, I can't control my eating."

Just to let her know that she's not crazy and that she isn't alone, I tell her that a lot of people hide to cheat, and that some people hide food in the most peculiar places - under their mattresses, in dresser drawers; in the tool shed, in the basement, anywhere. And they do it not because they're crazy, but because they feel guilty about doing something they know they shouldn't but can't resist.

She adds:

"It is true that the longer I hid there eating, the more I hated myself. That night I had nightmares about being so huge that a door frame had to be dismantled so I could get through. I don't think there's any hope for me. Even with all your care, I feel I'll never improve."

"Don't be such a pessimist, Frances. This is a perfect opportunity to get to know yourself better and to improve. Control of the emotions and behaviour is usually only achieved by understanding and correcting negative experiences. Use this experience to go forward. If you can learn something important about yourself, this can prove to be the most important week in your entire weight loss treatment. Actual weight loss per week is not the most important factor. The way you manage to modify your behaviour is much more important. A few pounds more or less at the end of the year is of little consequence. But once a person has learned to control a
158

certain behaviour or a habitual response, that person's life has permanently improved."

Then I explained her bizarre behaviour to her. Feeling justifiably proud about the way she'd dealt with the sugaring off party, she went home feeling she deserved a reward. Unfortunately, ever since she was a kid, reward has meant food.

Unfortunately, this is a widespread response in our society, and it is exploited and maintained by food industry advertising. It amounts to mass brainwashing. Recent studies reveal that, of the 26 hours of television the average person watches in a week, 3 and one half hours are devoted to messages suggesting we reward ourselves by eating or drinking some product. Personally, I don't feel anyone deserves to be fat, alcoholic, diabetic, or to have cancer or heart disease. Excess food or drink is a direct cause of all of these.

Frances interjects:

"But I hardly ever watch T.V., and I never buy their junky products."

"Even if it doesn't directly influence you, it can do so indirectly. Even if you don't buy the products advertised, it seems you have bought the notion that the act of consuming... is the road to happiness. And the logical corollary is that the more you eat the happier you are. I've met thousands of people who believe in that creed, and what I've observed is this: the more you eat, the fatter you become, and the more unhappy you are.

The other way advertising can have an indirect effect is by influencing the people around you who then become merchants of the notions of happiness through consumption: What a party! We ate so much we could barely stand up!"

She says:

"It's true, I did feel proud of myself, and when I got home, I did feel an irresistible compulsion to eat. And it's also true that, ever

since my childhood, reward has meant food. My parents had been deprived during the depression, and when prosperity returned after the war, they couldn't seem to give us enough. They treated every meal as if it might be the last for a month."

"It's natural to reward good behaviour, but doing it with food is an acquired habit."

"But how come I continued to cheat all week? Once I'd rewarded myself by eating all the cake, I shouldn't have had to go on."

She was right, it wasn't the need to reward herself that drove her to continue overeating, but the need to punish herself.

Feeling guilty for cheating, she hated herself, and to punish herself, she kept on eating. She adds:

"I was angry with myself all week. I called myself every name in the book. Names I'd be embarrassed to repeat. The way I felt comes down to this: So you want to eat, fatso. Well, go ahead, you don't deserve any better."

Guilt is a negative emotion. One brings it upon oneself, and it can only lead to negative behaviour and self-punishment. All of us set our own criteria and judge ourselves accordingly. That is why no two people will react exactly the same way in a given situation. One might feel the negative experience as a learning opportunity, the other, as cause for severe self loathing.

Personally, I don't think Frances should feel guilty about the way she behaved. She is a victim of her habitual responses. She should use this experience to study her behaviour and to determine how, the next time a similar situation arises, she may reward herself more appropriately.

Another thing I've often noticed is that people are harder on themselves than they are on others. They may be very understanding about certain behaviour when they see it in others, but judge themselves severely in similar circumstances.

Frances interjects:

"If I don't feel guilty when I cheat, how can I ever succeed?"

"What happens when we find someone guilty of a crime?"

"We hand down a judgement and a sentence."

"That's the very process that goes on in your own head. When you find yourself guilty you automatically, without any conscious thought, hand down a sentence. The more guilty you feel, the harsher the punisment, and the further it takes you from your desired reward: being thin."

"You're probably right. I've always had terrible guilt every time I cheat, and I haven't made any headway. Is it possible for a person to punish herself for several months over a single incident?"

"Absolutely. Depending on how severe we judge the crime to have been, we can punish ourselves for months or even years."

"Several months ago, at a party, a person commented on my weight while I was in the middle of eating. I became incensed and I struck out at him with my knife in hand. He required five stitches. I ate like a pig for three months. I had no idea what was going on with me. I thought I was losing my mind. But how could I get rid of my guilt?"

Getting rid of guilt feelings is not a matter of theory. You may know you shouldn't feel guilty; that won't change how you feel. The only way it can be done is by deprogramming techniques based on real situations. When you live through a situation that automatically gives rise to guilt feelings, you have to determine when you feel guilty, and then program yourself positively so that, the next time you're in a similar situation, you'll feel a little less guilty, and so on.

For example, Frances has learned from the cheating incident that she rewards and punishes herself automatically by eating. In order to break the habit or associating reward and food she not only has to stop eating, but she also must find a new way to reward herself, perhaps by buying herself an article of clothing, some perfume, a good book or a night out at a show.

Then she should program herself by repeatedly telling herself: "I'm allowed to cheat and I can improve by learning from my mistakes."

A Guilty Mother

A while ago I received a letter from a 54 year old woman named Lillian.

"I read your book "Be thin through motivation" and the testimonial in chapter 16 really made me think. I have a serious weight problem and I'm constantly dieting. Every time things seem to be going along just fine, something happens and I stop dieting."

"After reading your book I decided that this time nothing and no one would make me quit."

"Well, this week, my oldest son, he's a teacher and the father of a three year old, announced that he was getting divorced because his wife was 2 months pregnant. It seems he told her to get an abortion or he'd leave her."

"His wife wanted to keep the marriage together so they both went to see about an abortion. The doctor asked why my son wanted his wife to have the abortion and he answered that she had enough stretch marks. The doctor refused to recommend the abortion and suggested my son might want to see a psychiatrist."

"I'm sorry to have to say it, Doctor, but my son is an insensitive pig. I had eight children, and, in spite of my husband's drinking problem, they had everything they needed. I would never have dreamt of divorce."

"What have I done to deserve this? How did I fail so badly that I end up with such a son?"

"I was doing well with my diet but I've been eating out of control ever since I got the news. It's as if I felt I didn't deserve to be happy."

"There's no question I've failed miserably in bringing up my son. Will I ever be able to be forgiven, or am I going to have to live with this guilt all my life?"

"I'm sorry to bother you with my personal problems. You don't have to bother answering, just writing it down has helped."

Lillian's behaviour is easy enough to understand: she feels guilty about her son's behaviour, and she's punishing herself by overeating.

But is she really guilty?

She thinks so, but I would say she isn't.

To be guilty, you have to be fully conscious of what you're doing or saying. She didn't teach her son to be irresponsible. On the contrary, she was the very model of responsibility in bringing up 8 children practically on her own. So, on a conscious level, she always presented positive moral values.

Did she provide a perfect up-bringing? Only a perfect parent could provide a perfect up-bringing, and they tend to be a rare breed indeed. In a family situation in which she was more victim than anything else, she gave 110% of herself. She can't be faulted. Sure, with more experience she might have done some things differently, made different decisions. Maybe today she'd decide to have fewer children; perhaps she'd choose a different man. But we're not born with experience. It's acquired. It's the positive fruit of life's difficulties.

In order to succeed, Lillian will have to overcome the guilt she feels, particularly about her son's behaviour. She'll have to program herself by telling herself repeatedly: My son is an adult, and he has chosen what he feels is right. Since he won't listen to me, there's nothing I can do. His problems are his own. My energy is best spent dealing with my own problems.

163

A Guilty Father

When I was giving a talk to a group of businessmen, a well known local political figure asked me this question:

"I've put on a considerable amount of weight in the last two years, and yet I'm not eating any more than I used to. How do you explain that?"

"There are only two ways of putting on weight, by increasing your caloric input or by decreasing the number of calories you burn. Losing weight is the opposite process, you have to either decrease your input, or increase your output. Three food types account for an increase in body fat: fats, sugars and protein. Two factors can affect output, metabolic rate and exercise. In the last two years there's necessarily been a change in one of these factors."

"I have a friend who eats twice as much as I do and he never puts on weight. He's just lucky and I'm not."

"People who eat more than they burn off and still don't put on weight are very rare indeed. They are the exceptions that confirm the rule. They are the ones who are abnormal. They usually have a hyperactive metabolism either because of a thyroid disfunction, intense physical activity, or excessive stress. I've found that such people are often extremely highly strung, and they burn off a lot of calories from sheer nerves."

"I have a friend I've always envied," he replied. *"He eats like a horse and never puts on weight. I thought he was a very calm and relaxed guy. He was president of a medium size firm. But he cracked. He had a nervous breakdown and he hasn't worked in months. I still prefer my problem. But does stress always keep weight down?"*

"No. It can go either way. Some highly stressed people lose weight, others pack it on. I've heard a lot of people complain about putting on 2 to 4 pounds right after a stressful experience. What happens is not that they put on fat, but the stress hormones cause them to retain water. For the rest, habitual behaviour is the

determining factor. Some people eat more when they're under stress, others do the opposite."

Then he asked another question:

"Is alcohol fattening?"

"Ounce for ounce, alcohol contains almost twice as many calories as sugar. Also, especially if you drink before a meal, alcohol increases your appetite and lowers your willpower. A word of advice: give up the before dinner drink. A glass of wine with the meal will do a lot less harm. Don't forget beer, wine, and liqueurs all contain alcohol. Also when you add fruit juice or soda pop to alcohol, you just about double its calorie count."

The next day I got a call from the gentleman in question.

"I'd like to meet you somewhere other than your office. I know it seems a little unusual, but what I have to say is very confidential. You'll understand when you've heard what it's about."

We arranged to meet at a restaurant that evening.

"I'm sorry for all the mystery, but I wanted to explain why I've been putting on weight for the last 2 years. You see, 2 years ago my son announced that he was a homosexual."

"Isn't your son a doctor?"

"That's the one. Now you understand why I didn't want to risk any of your personnel overhearing our conversation. When he told me, I was devastated. After everything his mother and I had done for him. I just couldn't understand why he would do that to us. I threw him out. I haven't seen him in two years. Every day I wonder where I went wrong, how I managed to bring up a gay son. None of our acquaintances know, but every time the subject of homosexuality comes up I shudder. That's when I started drinking more and putting on weight. What should I do?"

"The first thing you have to do is get rid of the guilt you feel over your son's homosexuality. You are no more responsible for his sexual choices than you would be if he'd been born with big ears or a heart murmur."

"What's more, you should be proud of his professional achievements; he has an excellent reputation and his patients are very fond of him. His success speaks well of the education you provided for him. Now you have to accept his sexual orientation. You have to know it must have been very difficult for him as well. You might feel it would be better if he were otherwise but he isn't. Isn't it more important that he is happy being who he is than be unhappy pretending to be otherwise? He didn't take the easy way out, and you must accept who he is because he's made his choices and you're not responsible."

A few months later I met him at a political dinner. He was with his son. He was a new man. He'd lost all his excess weight, he was drinking in moderation, and he looked completely relaxed. At one point, when we were alone, he said: "You know what my son said the first time I invited him over to the house?"

"You're the best dad in the world. Thank you for accepting me as I am."

It's Always My Fault

Suzanne is 45. She chose to follow the 500 calorie diet with protein, vitamin and mineral salt supplements. It's a diet that naturally suppresses the appetite, so I was amazed last week when she said she often had terrific food cravings. I had her blow into the diet monitor which measures the level of ketones in the blood. The results showed she hadn't cheated. Logically, then, she shouldn't have been hungry. "You know, doctor, I'm not like everybody else. I must have done something wrong."

Then I analyzed her Bert results (my computer questionnaire on habits and behaviour). I discovered that she had a strong tendency to hypoglycemia, a low blood sugar. She said:

166

"My husband must be right, I'm not much good for anything. I can't even follow a simple diet. I always wake up full of good intentions. I skip breakfast, drink several coffees, and at lunch time I eat a little salad and cheese. My problems start toward the end of the afternoon. The kids come home from school. They are always quarreling and yelling and they hover around the kitchen looking for something to eat. Meanwhile, I'm supposed to be preparing supper. That's when I get a headache. I start to shake inside and I become very short tempered. It's around then that I get the cravings and my resistance is nil. I eat everything in sight and don't let up until I go to bed. I don't need a diet specialist. I need a psychiatrist."

Like many of my patients, Suzanne's problems were physiological and not psychological. In her case, hypoglycemia. The late afternoon symptoms she describes are not the result of her inability to deal with the chaos around her; they're caused by low blood sugar. And her blood sugar is low simply because she skips breakfast and eats very little for lunch. Simply recognizing how the body functions and feeding it a reasonable meal at regular 3 to 6 hour intervals will eliminate the hypoglycemia and the psychological problems caused by her guilt over her inadequacy in dealing with the after school hours.

The moment she begins to eat 3 healthy meals at regular intervals, she'll no longer have the headaches, the shakes, the cold sweat or the afternoon hunger pangs. She won't feel the compulsion to eat before supper and she won't feel the guilt and the need to punish herself all evening by overeating. If people ate three good meals a day at regular intervals, the case loads of many psychiatrists would be significantly reduced. Furthermore, no one who suffers from hypoglycemia can ever hope to lose weight or stay slim without eating three balanced meals a day. It's a problem that plagues many overweight patients and it should be looked into before referring anyone to a psychiatrist. Suzanne took my advice.

167

She got into the habit of eating three meals a day; her cravings disappeared immediately and she lost 55 lbs. within four months.

Then, with only 22 lbs. to go, she started to "yo-yo", losing a couple of pounds one week and regaining them the next. Two months later she hadn't made any progress.

In order to discover the nature of her motivation block, I had her take "Liza", my computerized psychological questionnaire. When she came back into my office after the test, she told me what was bothering her. It seems "Liza" had unlocked her secret.

"I've felt depressed for the past while. Things aren't going very well with my husband. He's always putting me down. He says I talk to the children too much and I didn't always tell the kids everything that was going on. He criticizes me for seeing a doctor about losing weight. He says I'm going out of my mind. He won't talk things over; he thinks it's childish. He figures he doesn't need a shrink. He blames everything on me and sometimes I wonder myself. Other times I feel I've had enough and that we should split up. He is unbearable. Even my children tell me I should leave him. But even though it's been a hard 20 years, I can't see myself alone. It's not money; I've got a good job. And the kids have said they'd come with me. I really feel it would be better for me and the kids, but something won't let me do it."

Suzanne's problem was that she felt guilty about marrying her husband when she never really loved him.

"I was 28 and I'd always wanted kids. I met this man who was an ex-priest. I didn't really love him, but I had a lot of affection for him and I thought that with time and children my feelings would grow. After dating for six months we got married."

Soon after they were married, she realized that he wasn't a particularly sexual person. Since the children were born, they had had sex only 3 or 4 times a year.

"I think he might be homosexual. I tried to bring it up once, but

168

he won't listen. Ultimately, the whole thing is my fault. I wasn't in love with him, and I shouldn't have married him. So now I just have to live with it."

Suzanne feels guilty about having married a man she didn't love and she's been punishing herself for twenty years by continuing to live in an unhealthy situation.

In order to enjoy some of the happiness she deserves, and to reach her ideal weight, she'll have to get rid of her guilt. She did decide to marry the man, but she isn't guilty of the failure the marriage turned out to be. For twenty years she has tried to improve and save her marriage. It's her husband's complete lack of cooperation that has led to its constant deterioration. As for the lack of love she feels guilty about, it's been my experience that love does indeed grow over the years through shared experiences. The original youthful passion is just a beginning stage.

As a deprogramming strategy I suggest she repeatedly tell herself: "The fact that I made a mistake one day is no reason to punish myself for the rest of my days. I must learn from my mistake, and use it to improve my life." Six months later, I saw her again. She was radiant, but she was still carrying her 22 extra pounds. *"I finally left him. My children are with me. Things are great. They are much calmer, and they are doing very well in school. I'm really quite proud of myself. I still eat three well balanced meals a day, and in spite of all the trauma around my separation, I didn't put on any weight. I've come to see you about losing the last few pounds, and I know I'm going to make it."*

Summary

Guilt is a negative feeling. It stops its victim from making progress.

People feel guilty when they feel they have done something that doesn't live up to the standards they've set for themselves.

169

Two people can do the same thing in similar circumstances and feel entirely   differents about it. One can be enthusiatic about the learning opportunity the experience represents while the other may feel guilty and resort to self-punishment.

The difference arises from the fact that each of them has different standards; they think differently about the situation.

Our standards come from a variety of sources. Our parents represent the first and often the most lasting influence in their development. As children we are without resources and we consider our parents to be infallible; they are therefore empowered to impose whatever standards they want, good or bad. These become our own, and they are tenacious. School, church, government, advertising, friends, spouse, children, all of these tend to affect the standards we set for ourselves.

After evaluating the answers of thousands of patients to our computer questionnaires, "Bert" and "Liza", I've come to the realization that fully 75% of them suffer from the poison of guilt.

We must put a **STOP** to it and accept that we are all human beings, subject to errors and imperfections, all of which, fortunately, can help us progress along the road to a full and satisfying life.

The encouraging thing is that we can overcome guilt.I've seen hundreds of people do it using deprogramming techniques.

It's simply a question of formutating a sentence appropriate for dealing with a specific guilt producing situation and repeating it to yourself frequently every day for at least 21 days.

To increase your chances of success you might want to try different methods of repetition: autogenous suggestion, self-hypnosis, alpha state relaxation, daily writing of the sentence, recording the sentence and playing it throughout the

170

day during daily routines or even when you're sleeping. For more details I refer you to my book *"Be thin through motivation"* and particularly to the chapter on the power of words.

Frances couldn't understand why she had behaved as she did. The experience provided a perfect learning opportunity. All her life she'd rewarded herself by eating. And, when she felt guilty, she punished herself by eating some more thus depriving herself of what she really wanted most: to be thin. She had to learn that the only way to progress and to get rid of guilt is through negative experience. After a given situation, guilt arises automatically, and we can't expect to be able to deal with it right away. It's the perfect time to examine and identify the thinking and the standards we apply to that situation. Then we have to modify or soften our thinking and our standards by using the programming techniques and the power of words and repetition. Frances programmed herself by telling herself repeatedly: I'm allowed to cheat and I can improve by learning from my mistakes.

Lillian wrote to tell me about the guilt she felt over having brought up a son who wanted to divorce his pregnant wife because of her stretch marks. She isn't responsible for her son's appalling behaviour. Every human being is only responsible for his or her own behaviour.

In the same way, the politician I met at one of my lectures had to learn to accept that he wasn't responsible for his son's homosexuality. Our children are independent human beings with a right to live their own lives and make their own decisions.

Suzanne wasted nearly 20 years of her life feeling guilty about marrying a man with whom she wasn't in love. Once she'd deprogrammed herself by repeatedly telling herself: "The fact that I made a mistake one day is no reason to punish myself for the rest of my days", and once she'd acquired the habit of eating three balanced meals a day at regular times, she was able to live a happy life as a single parent with her two healthy and happy children.

Personal Journal
to
Help You Control Your Emotions
"I Can't Take Criticism."

When you realize that you've eaten more than usual and that your overeating was the result of a disappointment or some other emotional trauma, examine your behaviour as follows:

Sequence: A: an external cause

B: triggered a thought process

C: which resulted in an emotional response and overeating.

Example: A: **My spouse criticized me.**

B: **I can't take criticism or accept the fact that I might be wrong.**

C: **I felt guilty and ate too much.**

YOUR NEW PROGRAMMING:
(to replace your old B sequence)

In future you would do well to tell yourself often: "I have the right to make mistakes and to be criticized."

Use the other page to write out your own A-B-C sequence whenever you experience an emotional upset this week.

Personal Journal
to
Help You Control Your Emotions

A: The external event that set it off.

_____

_____

_____

_____

B: What I thought about it.

_____

_____

_____

_____

C: My subsequent feelings and behaviour.

_____

_____

_____

_____

My new way of thinking and my new programming should be:

_____

_____

_____

_____

"Repeat" this new programming several times a day if possible.

"Repeat" it particularly when similar circumstances arise.

"Repeat" it as part of your relaxation program.

The more you repeat it the more effective it will be.

Repetition is Programming

CHAPTER 12

I NEED TO BE LOVED

He Left Me

"I'll never get there. I ate enough for two all week and I made myself throw-up three times. I was doing pretty well, but now it's all starting again." Nancy has just come into my office. She's 24 years old and she's about 11 or 12 pounds overweight.

"Usually, emotional stress is what brings on that kind of reaction," I tell her.

" The man I was living with left me. This is the second time It's happened. Nobody loves me. I don't know what I do to them. Even this last one - he was unemployed and a drunk and he still left me. I even told him he could bring his other girl friend to live with us. He just swore at me and said I was nuts. When he left I felt like he'd torn my heart out."

Nancy is deeply upset. She can't deal with this second rejection by a man. It's not so much losing someone she loves that upsets her, it's losing someone who loves her.

She feels that her worth as a woman depends on her being loved by a man. She links her worth to the love she receives from men. In order to progress, she'll have to go through three stages. First of all, before she can expect others to love her, she must learn to love herself. You learn to value yourself as you appreciate your own successes. And to acquire successes you have to set goals and work to achieve them. With these successes in your personal, family and work life, self-confidence and self-esteem will grow. I refer you to my book *"Be thin through motivation"*, chapter 21 *"On the road to success"*, in which I suggest ways of setting and achieving realistic goals. As for Nancy, I had her repeat to herself several times daily: *"I enjoy feeling good about myself, because I'm the most important person in my life."*

Secondly I asked her never again to make major concessions in her relationships with men. If she's an important person, she must respect herself and have others respect her as such. She must avoid relationships with men not deserving of her respect. It is much more important for her to love herself than to live in a destructive relationship.

Thirdly, her new attitude will attract more desirable men. She'll encourage herself in the coming weeks by repeating to herself: "If he doesn't love me, it's up to him, but he doesn't know what he's missing. I'll find someone better soon enough."

I'm Having Trouble With My Daughter

At 34 Jane is the mother of a 14 year old girl.

"I woke up in the middle of the night and found myself in front of the fridge. Within two hours I'd eaten 3 boxes of 12 "Mae West" and drunk 2 quarts of milk. I think I'm going crazy."

"Why did you do it?"

"I have no idea. I was sleeping soundly and I just woke up automatically."

"It could have been a response to something that happened the previous day."

After a moment she said:

"It happened last Saturday. The only unpleasant thing I can recall that happened that day was a fight I had with my daughter. But that's nothing new, we're always fighting."

"Exactly what happened last Saturday?"

She became increasingly upset as she answered:

"I'm just a servant around the house. I think I'm going to go on strike. Let's see if they learn to appreciate me when I haven't cooked a meal, cleaned up or washed or ironed clothes for a week or so. Then we'll see."

"But what actually happened that day?"

"My daughter and I were going to go shopping to get her a pair of tennis shoes. At the last minute, she got a call from a friend, made different plans with her and was about to leave me and go off with her friend."

"Then what happened?"

"I gave her hell and told her that was no way to treat her mother. I grounded her and confined her to her room. Don't you think I did the right thing, Doctor?"

"What happened next?"

"When I had calmed down, I said she could go out with her friend, but then she was mad, and she started yelling at me. She told me to go away and leave her alone. I don't know what to do with her, we're always fighting."

"That's almost certainly the incident that sent you to the refrigerator in the middle of the night."

She interrupted:

"But it had happened in the morning and by the time I went to bed I wasn't even thinking about it any more."

177

"That may be, but it was still in your subconscious mind. It's not unusual for feelings to surface like that, at night, when the conscious mind is asleep."

Jane's problem is that she won't accept that her daughter is becoming independent of her. She sees her daughter's need to assert herself as a rejection, as a withdrawal of love.

"I've done my best for my daughter and I can't stand for her to treat me that way."

I suggested the following 4 steps to help her resolve her problem with her daughter. First she has to reinterpret the situation. Her daughter's behaviour represents neither rejection nor a lack of love. It's simply that her daughter is assuming her own identity and independence. Secondly, Jane will have to modify her own behaviour. Aggressive behaviour engenders aggressive responses, and harsh words only complicate matters. The love between mother and daughter is quickly lost in the spiral of invective. Thirdly, I suggested she begin to treat her daughter as an adult. I recommended she give her responsibilities within the home. In order to begin a positive dialogue I suggested she try the **DESC** method outlined in chapter 8. In order to maximize her chances I had her write down her DESC and give it to her daughter. It's sometimes easier that way when verbal communication has become difficult.

Finally I had her tell herself repeatedly every day: "My daughter is developing her own personality in a normal fashion; she's not rejecting me. I can suggest things to her but I can no longer impose my will on her. I accept that she is a separate person from me."

A month later, Jane was telling me:

"The other day for the first time ever my daughter asked for my advice. I was floored. A lot of her friends were smoking "pot" and having sex with their boyfriends. She didn't know what she should do, so she asked me how I felt. We had a long discussion. I've never

178

been prouder. My daughter really loves me."

What If He Doesn't Approve?

Rina and her husband are both dieting. She's 29, he's 30. In the same period of time, with both of them following the same diet, he lost twice as much weight as she even though she is much more overweight.

"It's depressing, Rina was saying. On the weekend my husband cheated more than I did, and he still lost weight, while I stayed the same. It's just not fair."

"There's nothing unusual about that, I'm afraid. First of all your husband's metabolic rate is statistically 15 to 20 percent higher than yours. That natural phenomenon alone means that he can consume about 250 calories more than you and maintain the same weight. Secondly, your husband is considerably bigger than you; he has a more massive body to feed. Even without considering his higher metabolic rate, the fact that he's 6 inches taller than you means he can consume 350 calories more than you before he starts to put on weight. Thirdly, he's more physically active than you are. His extra physical activity accounts for another 250 calories that you don't burn off. Taking all three factors into account, that's 800 calories more a day that your husband can consume before he starts to put on weight. So your husband can maintain his weight at 2300 calories a day while, to maintain yours, you have to keep your consumption down to 1500 calories."

"It still makes me mad. If I eat the same amount as he does and maintain his level of physical activity, I'll still put on weight while he loses."

"That's nature. Mind you, men have as much difficulty with weight problems as women, and obesity is a much more frequent cause of mortality among men than among women. It has been proven that the same amount of excess weight puts a much greater strain on a man's heart than on a woman's. Does that help?"

"Ever since my husband has come close to his ideal weight, I've

179

had the devil of a time losing with any regularity."

"How would you rate your willpower?"

"That shouldn't be any problem; I really want to lose; I have a lot of determination!"

"How about your motivation?"

"It's what I want most in the world. I'd give anything to lose weight and yet it's not working. Weekdays I usually have no problem sticking to my diet. But weekends and days off are terrible. Take last week, for example, my husband was on vacation. He'd just finished his diet and he wanted to go out for dinner every night. I couldn't turn him down."

I answered:

"You were right. You should go out even when you're on a diet. I think you should take advantage of any chance you have for a pleasant outing. Having to change your living habits and eat less is frustrating enough. You should take advantage of every possible opportunity to relax and enjoy yourself. However, you have to learn to do so while still maintaining control. The trick is to learn to order foods that fit into your weight loss diet. You should have explained to your husband that, while you were happy to go out, you wanted to stick to your diet, and you should have asked for his help in choosing the most appropriate restaurant."

"I didn't want to do this to him while he was on vacation."

"Do what to him? Wouldn't he simply enjoy your company? And don't you think he'd appreciate your efforts to stick to your diet? Besides you could order according to your diet, while he could order anything he wanted."

"He would feel uncomfortable if we did that. He can't understand why I'm not losing weight as quickly as he is. He just expects me to lose like he does."

"Have you ever considered asking him for his help?"

"No, never, she said, but he must realize I could use it. It must

180

be that he just doesn't want to."

"Your husband and you are entirely different. You don't think or feel the same way about things. You should never assume that he should know or see anything in the same way you do. You have to learn to express your needs. You should tell him your doctor explained that your metabolism is different from a man's and that you can't live as he does and still hope to lose weight. Beyond that, the best way to get someone's help is to give him a role in your treatment. Tell him losing weight is very important to you and that you absolutely need his help."

"Maybe I'll try that."

"Just say: Do you want to help me? and see what happens."

The next week her husband was in for his follow-up. When I asked about his wife he said:

"I don't know what her problem is. I've lost what I had to lose. Yet in the meantime, she's hardly lost any weight at all. Maybe she's cheating behind my back."

"Did she tell you about the conversation she and I had last week?"

"No."

"Did she ask you to help her with her diet?"

"No, she didn't. But I do the best I can, I know losing weight is something she really wants, and I'd like to see her do it too."

I explained why his wife couldn't lose weight as quickly as he, and why she couldn't cheat much if she hoped to obtain results.

"Rina never mentioned any of this to me," he said.

"I think your wife loves you very much and she simply doesn't want you to have to change any of your living habits."

"I see now that, not only wasn't I helping her, I might have been hindering her. I'll try to make up for that in the future."

Rina's problem is that she doesn't assert herself where her husband is concerned. She's afraid to lose his love if she expresses her needs or refuses him any of his wishes.

She doesn't realize that's the best way to lose him. By not asserting herself, and by living as an adjunct to her husband, she's denying her own personality. She's not accumulating any personal success, any self-worth.

She runs the risk of becoming increasingly weak, and of totally undermining whatever self-confidence and self-esteem she may have. The less she values herself the more frightened she becomes of losing her husband.

If you don't love yourself, you can't love someone else. You'll just keep looking for something in the other that you would be lacking within yourself.

Fortunately for Rina, her husband would like nothing better than to help her, but he still has to be asked.

Rina will have to learn to assert herself, to express her thoughts, her feelings and her needs, and to say "no" when she feels she should.

Her fear of losing her husband's love, insofar as it led to her self-abnegation was leading to the failure not only of her weight loss program but also of her marriage.

Needing love at all costs is the best way never to find it.

Rina must tell herself repeatedly: "The more I assert myself, the more I'll value myself, and the more I'll be loved for who I am."

Her husband might well respond: "I loved my original wife, but I love my new wife even more."

They Don't Love Me

Three years ago, Giselle came to see me about a weight problem. She was separated and had a 7 year old daughter who lived with her. Within two months she'd lost 15 pounds, but she soon regained them. She was a classic "yo-yo" case. She had a major problem at work that she simply could not resolve. One day she said to me:

"The atmosphere at work is unbearable. I work with about ten other women and they're always saying things about me behind my back. They don't like me. I can't stand it anymore. Even though I will hate to do it, I'm going to ask to be transferred to the night shift. That way I'll be left alone and I'll be able to stick to my diet a little better."

In order to find out why she was so bothered by the gossiping of her fellow workers, I asked her to keep a personal journal monitoring her feelings, and to try to think of events in her past that had triggered similar emotional responses.

The following week she told me she'd been able to define her feelings a little better: she felt rejected by the group. She'd had the same kind of feeling when her father died when she was thirteen, and later, when her husband left her.

These events had hurt her enormously, and after her separation she'd dealt with it by shutting herself in with her daughter. Aside from work and necessary shopping, she never left the house. That was how she chose to minimize the risk of another rejection.

But was that kind of isolation the best solution? In reality she was frustrated by her isolation, and her overeating was a response to that frustration. In addition, since her isolation was not complete, she could never entirely escape the threat of rejection. As a result of that threat, she had developed a cold and defensive attitude. She never smiled, and she was difficult to deal with.

Since we are entirely responsible for the way people see and treat us, she was reaping what she'd sown. A cold defensive attitude gives rise to a similar response. It has a boomerang effect. If her attitude says "I hate the world", she can hardly expect the world to love her.

"I can't stand it. I have to change work environments. I'm going to go on the night shift. I can't go on working in a situatiion where everybody dislikes me."

With those words she left my office, and I didn't see her again for several months.

In order to deprogram herself of her feelings of rejection Giselle would have had to reinterpret her father's death not as a rejection, but as a normal, and, inevitable event. He hadn't chosen to withdraw his love.

Secondly, her separation from her husband was not a rejection in the sense of a person rejecting something that's no longer any good. Right or wrong, her husband was free to chose a family life with her or not, and she had the same right. He chose to leave her, not because she wasn't worthy but because she hadn't managed to show her true qualities to him, or perhaps because hers were not the qualities he was looking for.

Nobody can reject someone else without that person's complicity.

With regard to the separation, the conclusion that she was unworthy was Giselle's own conclusion. She didn't have to see it that way, indeed she would have done well to see it otherwise.

As for her workplace, she was merely getting back from her co-workers the same cold attitude she was serving them. Didn't they have every right to dislike her since she disliked them? If you consider it in its simplest terms, the whole thing was just a communication problem.

In order to help herself deal with her work environment she might have adopted a smiling and interested attitude towards her co-workers, and repeated to herself: "Whether people love me or not takes nothing away from my basic worth."

Nine months later, Giselle was back in my office. She was looking great:

"I thought about what you told me. It wasn't easy to accept that I was the one who had to change, not the people around me. I read the books you recommended on the art of making friends, and I finally got it. I changed my attitude. Now I smile and express interest in other people. It's like a magic formula. The very first time I complimented one of the other girls on her work, which wasn't easy for me to do, she immediately acted differently toward me. She smiled and told me I was doing a good job too. Almost from one day to the next, the atmosphere at work changed dramatically. Now I enjoy meeting people, and I'll never again allow anyone or anything to undermine my self-esteem. People can like me or not, that's up to them, it has nothing to do with my worth as a human being."

Summary

Not everyone can love everyone else. That's easy enough to say, but often hard to cope with.

Only when you are dealing with a difficult situation can you deprogram yourself and accept it as a fact. Then you have to tell yourself repeatedly: It would be better if everyone loved me, but they have every right not to, and that takes nothing away from my basic worth.

Nancy couldn't deal with the fact that her boyfriend had left her. She was ready to make any compromise no matter how humiliating just to have someone around who loved her. What she didn't understand is that she had to learn to love herself before she could expect anyone else to love her. She deprogrammed herself by repeating: "If he doesn't love me, that's up to him, but he doesn't know what he's missing. I'll find someone better soon enough."

Liza couldn't accept that her daughter would choose to spend time with a friend rather than with her. She reacted by binging. By changing her attitude, by accepting her daughter's increasing independence as a normal development, and by writing out a DESC, she grew closer to her daughter who subsequently sought her advice on some very crucial questions.

Rina and her husband were on the same diet, and they couldn't understand why they were getting different results. Because she was afraid to lose her husband's love, she had never asserted herself or developed her own self-worth. To want love at any cost is the best way never to find it. "The more I assert myself, the more I'll value myself, and the more I'll be loved for who I am." That is what she has to keep telling herself if she wants to overcome her weight problem, feel good about herself and reconquer her husband.

Giselle had shut herself in with her daughter to avoid being rejected yet again. She had misinterpreted the significance of her father's death and of her separation. Fearing the threat of rejection, she'd adopted a cold and reserved attitude. In reality, she was only hurting herself by taking at face value the reactions and the words of others. "They can say whatever they want; they can like me or not, I don't have to accept their opinions." That's what she should have been telling herself. When she finally started to, she began to smile and show interest in others, and her life became much more pleasant.

Personal Journal
to
Help You Control Your Emotions
"You've Been Cheating."

When you realize that you've eaten more than usual and that your overeating was the result of a disappointment or some other emotional trauma, examine your behaviour as follows:

Sequence: A: an external cause

B: triggered a thought process

C:which resulted in an emtional response and overeating.

Example: A: **Tonight at dinner my husband said I'd been cheating on my diet.**

B: **I resented his meddling.**

C: **I was angry and ate even more.**

YOUR NEW PROGRAMMING:
(to replace your old B sequence)

It would be better if others didn't watch what I'm eating, but he was doing it to help. I'm not perfect and I'm entitled to cheat but not to give up.

Use the other page to write out your own A-B-C sequence,whenever you experience an emotional upset this week.

Personal Journal
to
Help You Control Your Emotions

A: The external event that set it off.

_____

_____

_____

_____

B: What I thought about it.

_____

_____

_____

_____

C: My subsequent feelings and behaviour.

_____

_____

_____

_____

My new way of thinking and my new programming should be:

_____

_____

_____

_____

"Repeat" this new programming several times a day if possible.
"Repeat" it particularly when similar circumstances arise.
"Repeat" it as part of your relaxation program.
The more you repeat it the more effective it will be.

Repetition is Programming

CHAPTER 13

THE LESS WE DO, THE BETTER

Changing Jobs

I met John, a childhood friend, at a party recently. I hadn't seen him in years. I remembered him as a very pleasant and enthusiastic person who loved to laugh. At 18, we'd been members of a successsful dance band, and we'd even cut a record. We spent a delightful evening recalling our youthful adventures.

However, all was not right with John. He was very happy to see me, but he seemed depressed, beaten down. His wife told me, in confidence, that he'd changed dramatically in the last year as a result of problems at work. She was worried herself, fearing the worst: a breakdown, unemployment.

Two days later I took it upon myself to call him and ask him if he could meet me to discuss his problems. He agreed.

John was employed by a large telecommunications firm. About a year earlier, the job he'd been happy to hold for seven years had disappeared as a result of an internal management shuffle.

It had been an administration decision that in no way called into question the quality of his work. John had been transferred to another department, but he just couldn't get used to it. At 41 he felt he was too old to learn a new job, and he thought his responsibilities had been diminished.

"I gave the company 18 years of my life, 7 doing an excellent job in my last position and they thank me by demoting me and giving me a new job to learn from scratch. It's just no fair. Corporations have no heart any more. I'll never be able to do it. I've been trying to get used to the new job for a year now, but it's taking much too long to learn, I've gotten too old."

I agreed that losing a job at which he'd excelled was certainly a disappointment, but, since he had no choice in the matter, he should seize the opportunity to prove that he could still succeed. The satisfaction of that success would do wonders for his self-esteem.

To keep himself motivated I suggested he work hard, do overtime and, if possible take upgrading courses. This was his answer:

"Why should I do that for the company? I gave them the best years of my life and look at what they did to me. I'd rather be unemployed. The company did offer me some courses, but I turned them down. From now on, the less I do for them the better."

"You didn't give them the best years of your life. You did a job you liked and that was fulfilling, and for which the company paid you. You were happy at your job, and that's the best payoff there is. What you have to do now is regain that kind of satisfaction in your new job. Happiness can only exist in the presence of personal satisfaction, which itself depends on successes. You've been unhappy for almost a year because you haven't had any success at work, in fact, with your defeatist attitude, you've been accumulating failures. If you want to enjoy life again, you have to start

190

experiencing new successes. You have to work hard and put in overtime, not for the company, but for yourself."

I suggested he tell himself repeatedly: "I can do it; I'm going into action; I'm going to become the most valuable member of my work team because it's important to me."

What was bound to happen did. John started working hard, took the courses, earned the respect and gratitude of his employers, but, more importantly, he regained his self-respect. When I saw him next, he was once again the joyful, and self-respecting man I'd known in my youth.

Talking Retirement

Carol, a lovely 35 years old woman, has come to see me about losing a few extra pounds. She's tall and quite slender, but as an ex-model, she can't tolerate even the slightest weight gain.

I find her tense and drawn. I have her take Bert, my computerized behaviour monitor, and find that she is highly stressed, in emotional turmoil, and very lonely. Liza, the other computerized questionnaire aimed at evaluating the causes of her behaviour reveals that she doesn't at all enjoy being a housewife. As it turns out, Carol is married to a man 12 years her senior. After a successful business career, he'd retired some 6 months before her visit. His plans were now to spend half the year in Florida and the other half at his country house and on the golf course.

"I'm going crazy," she said. *"I'm bored to tears. I've had to drop my modeling career because of my husband's new life. And he's so jealous he won't let me take another job, not even part time. He doesn't understand why I'm not satisfied with all the money we have and the year-round holidays. Maybe he's right. After all, doesn't everyone dream of having a pile of money and no responsibilities?"*

Carol was very upset; she didn't know what to think. In

191

the 6 months since her husband's retirement she had come to feel completely useless, and she couldn't stand to see her body begin to deteriorate.

Her reaction was very understandable; not very positive, but normal under the circumstances. Dr. Hans Selye, international authority in stress and a teacher of mine in 1965, used to say that stress wasn't bad in itself, but our reactions to it could be devastating. Indeed, stress is an essential part of life; without it, you're dead. Nor did he suggest we deal with stress by working as little as possible. On the contrary he wrote: "Hard work never hurt anyone, and in order fully to enjoy rest, you have to be tired." At 47, Carol's husband was tired from many years of hard work and he was ready to appreciate the relaxation of playing golf. But she was only 35, full of vitality and she couldn't take the inactivity that was being imposed on her. Her energy needed to be channelled into interesting, challenging and fulfilling work. Forced idleness meant self-destruction for her. Human beings are not meant to be idle. On the contrary, people find satisfaction and self-realization in achieving the goals they set for themselves.

If she was to feel satisfied with herself, Carol had no choice. She had to draw up a list of the things she could and would like to do. Then she would have to negotiate firmly and convincingly with her husband. The **DESC** technique introduced in chapter 8 is most appropriate in such situations.

A few weeks later she was saying:

"It wasn't easy. I thought carefully about all my options, given the circumstances, and I drew up a DESC and gave it to my husband. At first he was taken aback; he couldn't figure out what I wanted. I stuck to my guns and he finally agreed that I could work as an office manager for a company 3 days a week. He'll spend the winter in Florida, and I'll join him for a month's holiday. I've never felt better. I feel like a huge weight has been lifted from my shoulders. I'm glad things have worked out, because I truly love my husband. But if he hadn't accepted my plan I would have had to

leave him just to save my sanity."

Blaming Others

A while ago I participated in a televised panel discussion on the role of society in the problem of obesity. The audience was asked to vote by telephone on the question of whether society was to blame for the widespread incidence of obesity. Seventy five percent of the respondents answered "yes".

As the voting was taking place, we were debating the question on the air. One of the panelists was a 450 pound, 38 year old man. He seemed bitter and aggressive. His arguments may be summarized as follows: obesity is an illness beyond anyone's control. No doctor, no clinic, no product or medication can do any good. He spent his time blaming the government, hospitals, doctors, researchers, advertising and people who work in commercials for his condition. He concluded:

"If people would just leave me alone, I'd be a lot happier."

I was somewhat sympathetic to him, and I could understand his anger. He'd tried and failed three times to lose weight by fasting. This method has since been proven inefficient and inappropriate to the treatment of obesity. But I would'nt accept his defeatist attitude.

The treatment of obesity has come a long way in recent years. While in the past the emphasis was on getting rid of extra fat, to-day we treat the whole person: living habits, emotional state, stress, motivation and personality. Even getting rid of excess fat is now done much more efficiently with low calorie diets plus protein, vitamin and mineral salt supplements. Among subjects 30% or more above their ideal weight, only five percent manage to lose their extra weight on a 1,200 calorie supplement. At the American Society of Bariatric Physicians' annual meeting in 1983, which I attended in the company of 500 doctors from all over the world,

Dr. Thomas A. Wadden Ph D, a member of Dr.Albert J. Stunkard's University of Pensylvania research team, reported the results of a study comparing three types of treatment: balanced diet with appetite suppressants, behaviour therapy alone, and a low calorie diet with protein supplements plus behaviour therapy. After 18 months, only the protein supplement diet showed a significant weight loss, with a maintenance of about 75%. The other two treatments had shown little success,and the subjects on a balanced diet had all regained whatever weight they'd lost. He concluded that protein supplemented, very low calorie diets showed a lot of promise for the treatment of moderate and severe obesity.

After the televised panel dicussion, when I tried to explain the results of those recent findings to my recalcitrant fellow panelist, I ran into a brick wall. He wouldn't listen; he wouldn't even look at me. Yet his weight problem was not glandular he simply consumed 6,000 calories a day, two to three times what a normal person eats.

Marie-Odile Vezina, author of Mourir ou Maigrir (diet or die), was also on this panel. In her book she reports on interviews she recorded with dozens of extremely obese subjects who collectively had lost some 2,000 lbs. Men and women who had weighed 300, 400 and even 600 lbs.. and who'd managed to slim down to their desired weight.

Our fat co-panelist has chosen to stay fat. It's his choice and I respect it, but he must carry the responsibility for it squarely on his own shoulders and not blame others.

If he wants to be happier, he should stop pointing the finger at everyone else, and take himself in hand. Where there's a will, there's a way.

Summary

I don't think inertia ever yields happiness or serenity.

Human nature is such that we all need a reason to get up

in the morning, a sastisfying goal. The human body is an energy-producing machinek, and that energy has to be channeled into some form of activity. If it is bottled up it can literally cause internal damage. Pent-up energy is self-destructive. Consider a healthy child with nothing to do. It soon becomes restless and cranky, but within minutes of finding an interesting activity, he or she is transformed. Life becomes just fine, thank you.

My old friend John had shut in on himself as a result of a setback at work. He was doing as little as possible. For six months his energy remained unchanneled. As a result, he was on the verge of a nervous breakdown. I suggested he not only get to work, but that he work harder than ever, put in a lot of overtime and take some upgrading courses, not for the company but for himself; It worked. My friend became again the happy self-confident person I had known.

Carol, a 35 year old ex-model, was now forced into premature retirement because of the early retirement of her 47 year old husband who had decided to split his time between Florida and his summer cottage. Within a few months of this, she'd become very tense, and she's started to put on weight. In order to save her own health, she had to be firm with her husband whom she loved. She finally rejoined the work force and regained her health and physical shape. According to Selye, we can only enjoy rest when we've become suitably tired.

When I was doing a television panel show, one of my co-panelists was a 450 pound heavyweight. After three failed attempts at losing weight, he'd decided to give up and stay fat. He chose inertia even after he'd learned about the new protein supplemented diets and psychological treatments. Refusing to take responsibility for himself, he blamed everybody else for his problem. Until he changes his attitude, he'll never solve his weight problem, and he'll probably never be happy. And yet, many people with similar or worse weight problems have had great success.

Personal Journal
to
Help You Control Your Emotions
"The Less I Do."

When you realize that you've eaten more than usual and that your overeating was the result of a disappointment or some other emotional trauma, examine your behaviour as follows:

Sequence: A: an external cause

B: triggered a thought process

C: which resulted in an emotional response and overeating.

Example:　A: **My doctor wants me to read, to repeat things to myself and keep a journal in order to lose weight.**

B: **It's not fair that I should have to do all those things for the rest of my life just to lose weight. It's too much to expect.**

C: **I got discouraged and strayed from my diet.**

YOUR NEW PROGRAMMING:
(to replace your old B sequence)

The more I control my own fate, the more positive I am, the happier and the more self-confident I become.

Use the other page to write out your own A-B-C sequence, whenever you experience an emotional upset this week.

Personal Journal
to
Help You Control Your Emotions

A: The external event that set it off.

_____

_____

_____

_____

B: What I thought about it.

_____

_____

_____

_____

C: My subsequent feelings and behaviour.

_____

_____

_____

_____

My new way of thinking and my new programming should be:

_____

_____

_____

_____

"Repeat" this new programming several times a day if possible.
"Repeat" it particularly when similar circumstances arise.
"Repeat" it as part of your relaxation program.
The more you repeat it the more effective it will be.

Repetition is Programming

CHAPTER 14

Answering your questions

1. *Can a person be born just naturally emotional?*

The debate rages between those who claim that emotional makeup is hereditary, and those who say that it is acquired, beginning with our earliest relationship with our parents.

Personally I feel some of our predispositions may be inherited, but most of our emotional makeup is a result of our education and life experiences.

If you accept the idea that our emotional responses are a matter of genetics, you are accepting, by the same token, that we are powerless to change. Yet, in my practice, I've seen thousands of people take control of their stress and their emotions. In fact, with the help of Bert and Liza, (two computerized psychological questionnaires), I've been able to identify the causes of patients' emotional behaviour, and to monitor their progress in controlling their behaviour.

2. *I'm the only one of three children in my family to be so nervous. Why is that?*

While parents might be even-handed in their treatment of their children, each child interprets what (s)he hears and experiences in a unique way. And that's why there is no secret, miraculous, universal way to bring up children. Parents must ask themselves about each child: "How has (s)he interpreted what we said?" The child must be approached as an individual.

Recently, a nurse with two children, a boy and a girl, was wondering how it was that her 8 year old girl was very interested in her diet, while her 10 year old son didn't care at all. the answer came the day she reached her ideal weight. Her daughter said:

"It was my fault you put on weight. I'm really relieved and happy that you've reached the weight you wanted."

When the mother tried to find out why her daughter felt responsible, the girl answered:

"You always said it was your second pregnancy that started you putting on weight."

It had just been a careless comment, but it was enough to cause her daughter to feel guilty about her weight problem.

3. *If you're a nervous person, can you really change your nervous disposition?*

Even if you've always been a very nervous person, you don't have to live out your life that way. You have only one life to live, why not live it relaxed?

Today, we have at our disposal some very efficient means to achieve that. This book outlines some of the latest developments in the field. If you practice the techniques I have laid out for you, I'm sure you'll notice a dramatic positive change in yourself.

4. How long can it take to change one's emotional reactions?

Your emotional reactions can be triggered by any number of situations that set your thinking in a certain way. If you deal with each situation individually, and if you program yourself appropriately every day, you should notice a marked progress within 21 days. The idea is then to go on to the next emotional situation, and deal with it the same way. Many studies are being conducted right now in American Universities on the efficiency of this 21 days mental programming technique.

5. I worked on mental programming daily for at least 21 days, and yet I'm still just as nervous. Why?

If there is a conflict between your conscious and your subconscious, which is like a mental computer that stores only failures, the subconscious is usually going to win. That's what is meant by a "psychological block". In such cases, you have to identify the block and deprogram yourself, as I've described in my book "Be thin through motivation."

Once you've deprogrammed yourself and gotten rid of your block, the programming techniques will work effectively.

6. Why do no two people react the same way to an emotional situation?

Between the potentially emotional situation and an individual's automatic emotional reaction lies a thought process which necessarily differs from individual to individual.

We don't have the same emotional reactions because we don't think the same way. It follows that the best way to change negative emotional reactions is to change the way we think about the triggering situation.

7. You seem to attach a lot of importance to the process of recording emotional reactions on paper when they occur. Why is that?

In a given situation our emotional reactions arise automatically, before we even have time to think. It's a subconscious process. In order to understand the process, to control our emotional response, and to understand our thoughts about the situation, it's essential that we record the event, our emotional reaction, our behaviour and our thinking.

Only by becoming aware of what is going on in your head can you then take control of it. Otherwise you'll be one of those people who say: "I don't know what's going on with me. I feel as if there's nothing I can do. I must have been born this way."

8. Why is it so important to repeat the same sentences over and over?

At birth, the mind is like an empty box, or a computer that hasn't been programmed. You can only find in a box what's been put in there. Your computer is programmed by the words you repeat to yourself and hear repeatedly. The more frequently they are repeated, the more significant they become. The more we repeat them, the more they become habitual thought. Consider, for example, how often the same advertising messages are repeated in the print media, on radio and television. Each ad costs a fortune, but advertisers know it's money well spent.

Without repetition there can be no efficient programming. It's the key to success. Advertisers have been quick to learn that it's the only way to sway consumers. If it works for them, it can work for you.

9. I've learned self-control in a number of situations, but whenever I'm in a new situation, my old emotional reactions surface again, why?

That's absolutely normal. A new situation gives rise to a thought pattern that hasn't been changed or attenuated yet. In fact, it represents a fine opportunity for self-improvement. You can only achieve control over your emotions through negative experiences. They provide a reality base for new thought patterns. Negative emotional reactions provide the opportunity to go from the theoretical to true internal integration.

10. *Why am I sometimes upset by trivialities?*

Disproportionate emotional reactions to a minor problem arise because the problem recalls, often at an unconscious level, a previous very upsetting event.

Recently, I heard from a man who didn't understand why he couldn't stand the sound of a crowd cheering on the home team. In searching through his past he recalled being scared out of his wits while still in his playpen each time his father and older brother would cheer as they watched hockey on T.V..

11. *I had been in control of my nerves for several weeks when, all of a sudden, I panicked in reaction to the same old situation; why?*

That's normal; it's a flashback. Long after an emotional response has disappeared, it can suddenly reappear when you least expect it. However, it will be less intense and of shorter duration. You shouldn't let it discourage you; it's perfectly normal. It doesn't mean you have to start all over again from scratch. Keep repeating your positive sentences and get some rest, if you can. Often this kind of relapse occurs when you're tired.

12. *I don't see how I can ever be less nervous unless my husband changes.*

It is impossible to change others, we can only change ourselves.

Even when you are right in your critical judgments of others, you have to consider that they have every right to be wrong, and keep telling yourself: "IT WOULD BE BETTER if things were otherwise BUT I have to accept what I can't change."

Accepting what you can't change doesn't mean you stop asserting yourself. As important as it is to be able to express your feelings and your wishes, it is equally important to wish, but not to demand, that others change. Trying desperately to change someone else is not only a waste of time, it is a sure way to make yourself miserable.

13. *How can I use the psychological tests offered at the beginning of the book?*

These tests can be very important in that they give you a concrete evaluation of your current emotional state and stress level. They also allow you to monitor your progress. That's why I suggest you do them again after each reading of this book and every month. While the scale monitors your weight, these tests keep tabs on your emotional condition.

But don't forget to write your responses on a separate sheet of paper in order not to be influenced by previous responses. You'll be surprised to see the difference in your results from month to month, particularly if you put into practice the many techniques recommended in this book. Each of us is a new person each day.

Bert and Liza are more complex computerized questionnaires I use in my clinic. But the questionnaires contained in this book are sufficient, and will surely help you achieve your goals.

14. *How can I make the best use of this book?*

First, read it through once. The first three chapters explain the psychological process that lies at the heart of your emotional responses, and shows you how to control them.

The subsequent chapters act as a mirror and help you to see yourself more clearly. They will assist you in identifying your emotions and your thought processes in the context of real life experiences. They will also supply the programming and treatments appropriate to your situation.

If you have come to understand the importance of repetition, you will appreciate the value of re-reading this book several times. Make it your bed-side reading. Look up examples relevant to your experiences that day, review the thought processes, and practice the recommended techniques.

This book never ends. It's an open door for a better life. You'll be able to see a noticeable improvement within 21 days.

Re-read this book time and again, adapt the situations to your daily experiences and put into practice the recommended techniques and program. What you've always dreamed of, losing weight gently, without negative emotions, will soon become a reality. You will become a healthy and happy person.

TITLES AVAILABLE
FROM
DR. MAURICE LAROCQUE'S
HEALTH COLLECTION

Book
Be THIN through MOTIVATION

Unlike other weight-loss methods that usually only cause temporary results, this book will allow you, once and for all, to slim down without sliding back.

Dr. Larocque outlines a truly effective method of permanently eliminating the mental blocks of those struggling with weight problems.

MENTAL PROGRAMMING

This method is very easy to follow. With it, people have achieved remarkable results as evidenced by the numerous testimonials contained in this book.

Obtain the figure you've always dreamed about and enjoy life at last.

256pp.

Video Series

Using powerful teaching aids, computerized question-naires and professionally-acted role plays,Dr Larocque and his assistant, obesity specialist Peter Forbes, M.D., give you the simple, but effective tools you need to break out of the tiresome, frustrating "cycle of failure". They also show you how to remain motivated and perseverant whenever annoying obstacles get in the way of your goals.

Each video lasts about 30 minutes.

VOLUME I
How to program yourself positively

- Reach and maintain your ideal weight
- Look and feel better.
- Set realistic goals for yourself.
- Improve your self-esteem.
- Discover the effective tools you need to lead a happier, well-balanced life.

VOLUME II
How to overcome guilt

- Discover why you must distinguish between ambition and perfectionism.
- Eliminate fear of failure and other undesirable negative feelings.
- Recognize that it's o.k. to cheat occasionally while dieting.
- Mentally program yourself to reach your goals of the day, week, month and year.
- Use self-hypnosis to eliminate guilt and feel much, much better.

This series is available in VHS, BETA, 8mn.

AUDIO CASSETTE PROGRAM

Two albums of four cassettes each in a smart vinyl binder.

Program 1.
Be Thin by Suggestion

Autogenic relaxation and progressive relaxation; list of suggestions: how to eliminate guilt, and the taste for sweets and fatty foods; how to demystify the importance of food; and many other useful motivational devices.
Professional Speaker Richard Dagenais.

Program 2.
Be Thin, Be Motivated

Identify defeatism, negative and positive motivation, set realistic goals and achieve them, stay mentally young, how to unlearn old habit patterns, and much more.
Speaker: Peter Forbes, M.D.